Enid B

SUMMER
HOLIDAY
STORIES

Look out for all of these enchanting story collections
from **Enid Blyton** ...

Enid Blyton

SUMMER HOLIDAY STORIES

Hodder
Children's
Books

HODDER CHILDREN'S BOOKS

This collection first published in Great Britain in 2017
by Hodder and Stoughton Limited

3 5 7 9 10 8 6 4 2

Enid Blyton ®
Enid Blyton's signature is a Registered Trademark
of Hodder and Stoughton Limited

This collection copyright © Hodder and Stoughton Limited, 2017
Illustrations by Mark Beech copyright © Hodder and Stoughton
Limited, 2017

All of the author's moral rights have been asserted.

A CIP catalogue record for this book is available from the British Library.

ISBN 978 1 444 93278 2

Printed and bound in Great Britain by Clays Ltd, St Ives plc

The paper and board used in this book are made from wood from
responsible forests.

Hodder Children's Books
An imprint of Hachette Children's Group
Part of Hodder and Stoughton
Carmelite House
50 Victoria Embankment
London EC4Y 0DZ

An Hachette UK Company
www.hachette.co.uk
www.hachettechildrens.co.uk

Contents

The Goblin
Aeroplane

The Goblin Aeroplane

'IT'S SUCH a lovely day you can take your lesson books on to the hillside, if you like,' said Mummy one morning to Jill and Robert.

So out they went.

'What have you got to do?' Robert asked Jill.

'I've got to learn how to spell six words,' said Jill. 'They're rather hard. Here they are: "mushroom", "toadstool", "honey", "dewdrop", "magic" and "enchantment". Don't you think they are hard, Robert?'

'Yes,' said Robert. 'I'm sure I don't know how to spell them. I've got to learn my seven times table.'

'I'm only up to five times,' said Jill. 'Ooh, isn't it lovely out on the hillside, Robert?'

The two children sat down and opened their books – but it was hard to work. First a lovely peacock butterfly flew by. Then a tiny copper beetle with a shining back ran over Jill's book. Then a robin came and sat so near to them that they hardly dared to move in case he was frightened away.

'I say, Jill!' said Robert at last. 'How much work have you done?'

'None!' said Jill. 'Have you learnt your times table, Robert?'

'Only as far as seven times two,' answered Robert. 'It's a pity to have to do homework when the sun is shining so brightly and we'd like to play.'

'Well, let's not do it,' said Jill. 'No one will know, because we can take our books to bed with us tonight, and after Mummy has gone we can get them out and learn our words and our times tables then!'

'Oh, no, Jill!' said Robert, shocked. 'Mummy

trusted us to do our lessons here, and we must. It would be mean to play when she sent us out here for a treat.'

'All right,' said Jill. 'It would be mean – so let's get on quickly and finish them, Robert.'

The two children turned their backs on one another, put their fingers in their ears and began to learn their spelling and times table. They didn't look up once even when the robin flew down at their feet. They meant to do their lessons really properly.

Soon Jill sat up.

'I've finished, Robert!' she said. 'Hear my spelling, will you?'

'Yes, if you'll hear my seven times table,' said Robert. They passed each other their books, and Jill was just beginning to spell 'mushroom' when a very strange thing happened.

They saw a tiny speck in the sky, which rapidly grew larger. It was bright red and yellow.

'It's an aeroplane, Jill!' said Robert. 'But what a

funny one!'

It certainly was odd, for instead of having flat wings like an ordinary aeroplane, it had curved wings like a bird, and it flapped these slowly up and down as it flew.

'It's coming down!' said Jill, in excitement. 'Ooh, look, Robert, it's coming down quite near us!'

Sure enough the strange aeroplane flew swiftly towards them, flapping its odd red and yellow wings. From the cockpit a funny little man peeped out. He waved his hand to them.

The aeroplane suddenly dipped downwards, and with a whirr of wings that sounded rather like a giant bee buzzing, it landed on the hillside near the excited children. They ran up to it in astonishment.

'What a tiny aeroplane!' cried Robert. 'I've never seen one like that before!'

'It's a goblin aeroplane!' said the pilot inside, peeping at them and grinning widely. 'It belongs to me.'

'Are you a goblin then?' asked Jill, in surprise.

'Of course,' said the strange pilot, and he jumped out of his plane. Then the children saw that he really was a goblin. His ears were pointed and stuck out above his cap. His body was round and fat, and his feet were as pointed as his ears.

'I've come to ask if you can tell me where Greenfield Farm is,' he said.

'Oh yes,' said Robert. 'It's over that field, then through a path in the wood, then over a stile, then down by the stream, then over the little hill, then—'

'Goodness!' cried the goblin, 'I shall never find it in my aeroplane! Can't you tell me how to get to it from the air?'

'I might, if I were in your aeroplane with you,' said Robert, doubtfully. 'I think I should know what the farm looks like, but I couldn't quite tell you now how to go. You see, I've never been in an aeroplane.'

'Well come for a ride in mine,' said the goblin, grinning. 'You and your sister can both come, and as soon as you show me Greenfield Farm and I land there, you can hop out and run home again.'

'Ooh!' shouted both children in excitement, and they danced up and down in glee. 'Do you really mean it?'

'Of course,' said the goblin. 'Come on, hop in.'

So they climbed into the aeroplane, and the goblin climbed in too. Jill and Robert looked to see how he flew it. It was a very strange aeroplane, there was no doubt of that. In front of the goblin's seat were dozens of little buttons, each with something printed on. One had 'Down' on, one had 'Up', and another had 'Sideways'. Still another had 'Home' on, and a fifth had 'Fast', and a sixth one 'Slow'. There were many more besides.

The goblin pressed the button marked 'Up' and the aeroplane began to flap its strange wings. It rose from the ground, and the children clutched the sides in excitement, for it was a very odd feeling to be in something that flapped its wings and flew into the air.

'There's the farm!' cried Robert, and he pointed to a pretty farm house over to the east. At once the goblin pressed a button marked 'East', and the aeroplane flapped its way to the right. Soon it was over the farm, but to the children's great surprise it didn't land, but flew straight on.

'Aren't you going to land?' asked Jill. 'You've passed right over the farm.'

'Ha ha!' laughed the goblin, and it was such a nasty laugh that the children looked at him in surprise.

'Why don't you land?' asked Robert. 'I don't want to go too far, you know, because of getting home again.'

'You're going to come with me!' said the goblin. 'You didn't suppose I really wanted to go to the farm, did you? Why that was only a trick to get you both into my aeroplane!'

The children sat silent for a minute, they were so surprised. Jill felt frightened.

'What do you want us for?' asked Robert at last.

'To sell to Big-One the giant,' said the goblin. 'He's lonely in his castle and he wants two children to talk to.'

'But, good gracious, you can't do a thing like that!' cried Robert, in a rage. 'Take us back home at once, or I'll make you very sorry for yourself!'

The goblin smiled a wide smile, and said nothing. Robert wondered what to do. He did not dare to hit the goblin, for he was afraid that the aeroplane might fall. So he just sat there frowning, holding Jill's hand tightly, for he saw that she was frightened.

After about twenty minutes Robert looked over the side of the aeroplane. Far below was a strange-looking country with palaces gleaming on hills, and castles towering high.

'It must be Fairyland,' whispered Jill when Robert pointed it out to her. 'Oh, Robert, this is a great adventure, even if that old goblin is taking us to a giant!'

Just then the aeroplane plunged downwards, for the goblin had pressed the button marked 'Down'. It flew to a great castle standing on a mountain top, and landed on one of the towers. The goblin leapt out and ran to a staircase leading down from the roof.

'Hey, Big-One!' he called. 'Here are two children for you! Where's that sack of gold you promised me?'

Robert and Jill heard great footsteps coming up the stairs, and a giant's head peeped out on to the roof. He had a huge shock of hair, a turned-up nose, a wide mouth and very nice blue eyes as big as dinner plates. The children liked the look of him much better than they liked the goblin.

'So these are the children,' said the giant, in a loud booming voice. 'Well, they look all right, goblin. You can have your sack of gold tonight. I haven't any by me at the moment. Come for it at six o'clock.'

'All right,' said the goblin, and he went back to the aeroplane.

'Climb out,' he ordered, and Robert and Jill climbed down from the cockpit, feeling very strange. The goblin leapt into his seat, pressed the button marked 'Up' and disappeared into the sky, shouting that he would be back that night at six o'clock for his sack of gold without fail.

The giant looked at the two children.

'Will you come down into my kitchen?' he said, in a kind voice. 'I am sure you want something to eat and drink after your ride.'

Robert and Jill felt glad to hear him speak so politely. He couldn't be very fierce, they thought. They followed him down the enormous stairs and came to a vast kitchen where a huge kettle boiled loudly on a great fire.

'Sit down,' said Big-One, and he pointed to two chairs. But neither Robert nor Jill could climb on to the seats, for they were so high up. So the giant gently lifted them up, and then took the boiling kettle from the stove.

He made some cocoa in three great china cups, and set out three enormous plates, on each of which he had placed a very large slice of currant cake.

'Please join me in a little lunch,' he said. 'It is really very kind of you to take pity on me and come to live with me. I didn't think any children would be willing to come here, you know.'

'Why, we weren't willing!' said Robert, in astonishment. 'The goblin got us here by a trick. We didn't want to come here at all!'

'What!' cried the giant, upsetting his cocoa in his surprise. 'Do you mean to say that nasty little goblin brought you here against your will?'

'Yes,' said Robert, and he told Big-One all about the morning's happenings.

Jill listened and nodded her head, eating her currant cake, which was really most delicious.

The giant was terribly upset when he heard about the trick that the goblin had played on the children.

'I don't know what to do!' he said, and two big tears stood in his saucer-eyes. 'I wouldn't have had such a thing happen for the world! Now, however can I get you back again? And oh, dear me, that nasty goblin will be coming for his sack of gold too, and I haven't any. You see, I thought you'd be able to help me with my spells, for children are very clever – much cleverer than stupid giants like me. I thought I'd get you to help me with a gold-spell, and make some gold before the evening.'

'Well, we don't mind helping you a bit,' said Robert, who liked the big giant very much. 'Don't cry. You've splashed a tear into your cocoa, and it will make it taste salty.'

'Will you really help me?' cried Big-One. 'Oh, you good, kind children! Well, I'll just clear away these things and then we'll set about making a gold-spell.'

He put the cups and plates into a huge sink and washed them up. Then he took the children into a big bare room with many chalk circles drawn on the floor. A big pot hung over a fire that burnt with strange green flames.

'Now first of all I've got to write six words in the biggest of these chalk circles,' he said. 'But, oh dear me, I don't know how to spell them! Still, children are very clever, so I do hope you'll be able to help me. Can either of you spell "mushroom"?'

'I can!' cried Jill, excitedly. 'I learnt it this very morning! M-U-S-H-R-O-O-M!'

The giant carefully wrote it down in the circle as Jill spelt it. Then he looked up at her.

'Now could you spell "magic"?' he asked.

'Yes!' said Jill, 'M-A-G-I-C! That was one of the words I had to learn this morning, too!'

Well, would you believe it, all the words that the giant needed for his spells were the very ones Jill had to learn! Wasn't it a good thing she had done them so well? The last one the giant wanted was "enchantment".

'That's the hardest one,' said Jill, and she frowned. 'Oh, I do hope I remember it properly. Let me see – E-N–'

'Where's your spelling book, Jill?' asked Robert, terribly afraid that Jill might spell the word wrong after all. 'You could look it up before you spell it.'

'We left both our books on the hillside!' said Jill. 'No, I must try and spell it out of my head. Let me think for a minute – yes, I think I've got it. E-N-C-H-A-N-T-M-E-N-T!'

Big-One wrote it carefully down. Then he drew a toadstool and a mushroom right in the very middle of the circle, put a spot of honey on each, and shook a dewdrop from a piece of grass on to the honey.

'That's all ready for the spell now!' he said. 'What a good thing you knew how to spell "mushroom", "toadstool", "honey", "dewdrop", "magic" and "enchantment", Jill. But oh, dear me – the next thing we have to do is very hard!'

'What's that?' asked Robert.

'Well, two of us have to dance round the circle holding hands,' said the giant, 'whilst one stands in the middle chanting the seven times table. But I don't know the seven times table. I only know twice times.'

'I don't know it either,' said Jill.

'But I do!' cried Robert. 'I learnt it this very morning. I can say it! I'll be the one to stand in the middle.'

'Oh, good!' said Big-One, and he rubbed his great hands together in delight. 'Now listen – Jill and I will dance round together, and you must stand still in the middle saying your seven times table at the top of your voice. At the end of it I have to say twelve very magic words, and then, if we've done the spell right, a sack of gold appears right in the middle of the circle!'

'Come on, let's do it!' cried Jill. 'Are you sure you know all your seven times perfectly, Robert? It might spoil the spell if you got something wrong.'

'I'm not quite sure of seven times twelve,' said Robert. 'I think it's eighty-four, but just wait a minute and I'll work it out to make sure.'

He took a piece of the giant's chalk and wrote the figure 12 seven times on the floor. Then he added them up, and sure enough, it made eighty-four, so he was quite right.

Then they started the spell. Jill and the giant danced round the circle, and Robert stood in the middle saying his seven times table at the top of his voice. When he had finished the giant shouted out a string of curious magic words, and all the words he had written inside the ring suddenly vanished!

Then crash! A great sack suddenly appeared in the middle of the circle and knocked Robert down. He was up in a minute, and peeped into the mouth of the sack.

'Yes, the spell has worked!' he cried. 'It's full of gold! Ooh, what powerful magic! And what a mercy I knew my seven times table properly!'

The giant was so pleased. He could hardly thank Robert and Jill enough.

'You don't know how grateful I am to you,' he said. 'I can pay that horrid goblin now, though I don't think he deserves a penny, because he brought you here by a trick. But the next thing is – how am I going to get you home again?'

'I don't know,' said Robert. 'Could you use magic, do you think?'

'No,' said Big-One. 'I don't know any that would

take you home. Wait a minute – let me think.'

He sat down on a stool and frowned for five minutes. Then he jumped up and clapped his hands so loudly that it quite frightened Jill.

'I've a fine plan!' he said. 'The goblin will come in his aeroplane tonight at six o'clock. Now listen – I'll hide you behind a chimney pot on the roof of the castle. When the goblin arrives I'll call him downstairs to the cellar to fetch his gold. As soon as he's gone down the stairs you must pop out, jump into the aeroplane and fly home!'

'But we don't know how to fly a goblin aeroplane!' said Robert.

'Oh, it's quite easy,' said Big-One. 'Didn't you see all those buttons? Well, you just press the one that says "Up" and then the one that says "Home", and then the one that says "Down" when you see your home, and there you are!'

'Well, I think I could do that,' said Robert. 'Anyway, I'll try. But what shall we do till six o'clock?'

'Perhaps you'd like to come out with me in my yellow motor car and see the sights of Fairyland?' said the giant.

'Ooh, yes!' cried the children. So the giant took them out to his great motor car, and they climbed into it. What a time they had! They saw elves and fairies, brownies and gnomes, pixies and witches, and all kinds of strange little folk. They went into glittering palaces, they had dinner with a wizard and tea with a brownie, so you can guess what a glorious day they had. They were sorry when half-past five came, and the giant took them back to his castle.

He took them up to the roof and showed them a chimney to hide behind. Then he shook hands with both of them, and thanked them very much for all their help.

'Thank you for the lovely day you've given us,' said the children. 'We only wish we could stay longer, but our mother would be worried if we did.'

'Sh! Here comes the goblin!' said Big-One,

suddenly. He ran down the stairs, and the children were left alone behind their chimney. They heard a whirring sound, and saw the red and yellow aeroplane flying down, its strange wings flapping as it came.

The goblin landed neatly on the roof and ran to the stairs.

'Where's my sack of gold, Big-One?' he cried.

'Come down and fetch it!' came the giant's booming voice. 'It's in my cellar.'

The goblin raced down the stairs. As soon as he was gone Robert and Jill ran to the aeroplane and climbed into it. Robert pressed the button marked 'Up', and the aeroplane at once rose upwards. Then he pressed the button marked 'Home', and the machine turned round in the air and flew steadily towards the setting sun.

Jill looked back and saw the goblin standing on the roof of the castle, shouting wildly. The giant stood beside him, laughing. They could hear his great 'Ho-ho-ho' for a long way.

The aeroplane flew steadily onwards. Suddenly Jill gave a cry and pointed downwards.

'There's our house, Robert!' she cried. 'Press the "Down" button quickly!'

Robert pressed it. The aeroplane swooped down and landed on the hillside where the children had sat learning their lessons that morning. Robert and Jill jumped out, picked up their books which were still where they had left them, and raced home.

'Why, my dears, wherever have you been?' cried their mother. 'I have been so worried about you!'

'Oh Mummy, we've had such an adventure!' cried Robert. 'We've been up in a goblin aeroplane!' And he told her all that had happened. Their mother was so astonished that she simply couldn't say a word.

'Come and see the aeroplane,' said Robert. 'It's out on the hillside.'

They all three ran to the hill – but just as they got there they heard a whirring sound and Robert pointed up in the air.

'There it goes!' he cried. 'I expect it's gone back to the goblin. Oh, Mummy, I wish you'd seen all the buttons inside, and had come for a ride with us.'

'But that's not an aeroplane,' said their mother. 'It's only a very big bird. I can see its wings flapping.'

'No, really, it's the goblin aeroplane,' said Jill. But I don't think their mother believed it.

'Anyhow, my dears,' she said, as they all went home again. 'What a very good thing it was that you were good and learnt your lessons properly this morning – else you might have had to stay with that giant!'

And it was a good thing, wasn't it?

Billy-Bob

has a Surprise

Billy-Bob has
a Surprise

BILLY-BOB AND Belinda knew all the birds in their
garden. Outside their dining room window Daddy
had put a bird table, and on it each morning Billy-Bob
put the crumbs from the breakfast-cloth. At dinner
time Belinda scraped out the milk-pudding dish and
gave the birds the bits.

So you may guess that the birds liked Billy-Bob
and Belinda, and sang and chirruped in their garden
all day long. They didn't like Wags so much, because
sometimes, when nobody was looking, he climbed up
on to the bird table, by jumping on a flower-tub first,
and licked up the milk-pudding bits.

One day Billy-Bob saw a sparrow flying across the garden with something hanging from its beak. 'Look, Mother!' he called. 'What is that sparrow doing?'

'It is building its nest, Billy-Bob,' said Mother. 'All birds build their nests now, because it is springtime.'

'Oh, Mother! Will it build its nest in our garden?' cried Billy-Bob. 'What fun!'

'I want to see a sparrow with something in its mouth too,' said Belinda, looking out of the window.

'There goes one!' said Billy-Bob as another sparrow flew by with a long piece of straw in its beak. 'Oh, Belinda, let's put on our hats and coats and go out into the garden to see where the sparrows are building.'

So out they rushed. The sparrow was building a big untidy nest under the roof by the kitchen. It said, 'Chirrup, chirrup!' when the children watched it, and was not a bit frightened. It knew quite well that they were the kind children who gave it crumbs each day.

'Now let's go round the garden and see if we can find any more nests being built!' said Billy-Bob.

'It's so nice of the birds to build here. They know they are safe, for we won't take their eggs.'

They hunted all over the garden – but they could only find one more nest – and wherever do you suppose it was?

It was in the honeysuckle hedge that grew on one side of Belinda's own little garden! She saw a little brown bird fly in there and she ran to look – and there, tucked into the honeysuckle's fresh green twigs, was the neatest little nest!

'Billy-Bob, Billy-Bob, come and see! The birds love me! They have built a nest in my own garden!' shouted Belinda, dancing up and down on her fat legs.

Billy-Bob peeped at the nest. It belonged to a small, brown bird. It was a hedge-sparrow – not a noisy house-sparrow – but a little quiet brown bird with a beak like a robin's. She sat on her nest and looked at the peeping children, quite unafraid. She knew they were her friends.

'Mother! Mother! Come and see!' shouted Belinda.

Wags thought there must be a bone or a biscuit somewhere in the honeysuckle hedge to make Belinda so excited, and he jumped high in the air to see.

When Mother came to look, the little brown bird flew off her nest.

'Oh! Oh!' cried Billy-Bob and Belinda – for in the nest lay five eggs as blue as the spring sky! They were the prettiest sight.

'You mustn't disturb the nest,' said Mother. 'Belinda, you are very lucky to have a bird building in your own little garden.'

'They love me, they love me!' cried Belinda. 'Get down, Wags. They are my own birds, and my own nest and my own dear little blue eggs.'

Billy-Bob looked solemn.

'Mother,' he said, 'do you think the birds will build in *my* garden too?'

'They may not,' said Mother. 'You must wait and see.'

'Don't they love me as much as they love Belinda?'

said Billy-Bob. He couldn't help feeling rather hurt about it. He did give them crumbs too – and once he had given them half of his biscuit.

'Oh, yes, darling,' said Mother. 'Of course they do. But perhaps your garden hasn't such a good place for building a nest in, as Belinda's.'

'It has a honeysuckle hedge too,' said Billy-Bob. 'Well, I shall look every day and see if any bird is building in *my* garden. They must, they must, they must!'

But you know, they didn't! It was most disappointing. Belinda's little bird-family hatched out of the blue eggs, and became tiny little nestlings that opened wide beaks whenever the mother or father bird flew up with food.

'I have a bird-family of my own,' Belinda told everyone very proudly. 'The birds love me, and they have built a nest in my own garden.'

Billy-Bob was not at all happy about it. He and Wags hunted carefully every day in his garden, but never a bit of nest could they see – not even in the very thickest part of the honeysuckle hedge. Wags didn't really know what they were looking for – but it didn't matter. He hunted just the same, his short tail wagging nineteen to the dozen, and his red tongue hanging out of his big mouth.

'You can have half my baby birds, Billy-Bob,' said Belinda, when she saw how sad he was.

'No, thank you, Belinda,' said Billy-Bob, 'I like you to have all yours – only I do wish the birds loved me enough to trust me, and build in my garden, too.'

'Billy-Bob, the birds don't think about that when they build in any special place in the garden,' said Mother. 'They like you both very much – you are kind to them. It was just by chance that they built in Belinda's garden.'

But Billy-Bob felt quite sure that the little hedge-sparrow hadn't built her nest there by chance. She had built it there because she loved Belinda.

'Now, don't worry any more,' said Mother. 'Go and

get your spade and pail out of the summer-house and run to the sandpit and dig. Make a house with stones for windows, and bits of grass in the garden.'

So Billy-Bob ran to get his spade and pail. He remembered where he had left them – in the summerhouse at the back. He went in and saw his spade standing up. He looked for his pail. There it was.

But it was full of something. How funny! Billy-Bob bent down to see what was in it. And then he gave such a shout! He picked up his pail and walked carefully down the garden path, shouting, 'Mother! Belinda! Wags! Come and see! A robin has built her nest in my pail! Oh, do look! The birds love me too!'

Mother came running. Belinda trotted up. Wags galloped round, excited.

'Oh, darling!' said Mother. 'You have brought nest, eggs, robin and all! Take them back quickly to the summerhouse, or the robin will be afraid and will desert its eggs!'

'It won't be afraid of *me*,' said Billy-Bob happily. 'It is my own little robin. Its nest is made of roots, dead leaves and moss. Look, Belinda – it is a very cosy nest. I wonder how many eggs there are!'

'Billy-Bob, take it back,' said Mother. So Billy-Bob and Belinda took the pail back, carrying the nest, eggs and bird in it very carefully. The robin flew off when they put the pail down in the summerhouse, and sang a little creamy song from the window-sill.

'There are five white eggs with red spots!' cried Billy-Bob. 'Oh, I'm so excited. It's nice to have a nest in a honeysuckle hedge, Belinda – but don't you think it's nicer still to have one in my own pail?'

'Yes,' said Belinda. 'I do. The birds must love you a *lot*, Billy-Bob.'

Wasn't it nice for him?

First Walk in July

First Walk in July

'UNCLE MERRY, is it true that if it rains on St Swithin's Day it will rain every day for forty days, and if it doesn't it will be fine for forty days?' asked John, leaning on the wall between his garden and Uncle Merry's.

'Well, we'll see, shall we?' said Uncle Merry, looking up from his work. 'St Swithin's Day is on a Saturday, so we will plan a walk then, and keep a watch to see that it doesn't rain.'

'It's the thirteenth today,' said John. 'Two more days till St Swithin's, which is the fifteenth. I'll tell the others. They *will* be pleased about the walk, because there is a tremendous lot to see now in the countryside, isn't there?'

'I should just think so!' said Uncle Merry. 'For one thing there are over seven hundred different flowers to be found – even more than there were last month.'

'Oooh,' said John, 'if we found them all, what a big flower chart I should have to make!'

The night of the fourteenth was queer and overcast. Mother said there was going to be a thunderstorm. The children were upset, because they badly wanted the whole of St Swithin's Day to be fine, and if it rained after midnight, then that would count as St Swithin's Day.

The storm broke when they were in bed, about half-past nine. They were all asleep, and the first enormous crash woke them with a jump.

The thunder rolled and the lightning flashed. Janet usually made a silly fuss when there was a storm, but this time she didn't. She stood at the window with the others, watching the magnificent lightning. She didn't want Pat to tell Uncle Merry that she squealed at storms.

Then the rain came. What a rain! It poured down as if some giant in the sky was emptying bucket after bucket.

'Oh, dear,' said Janet in dismay. 'I'm afraid it will go on all night long – and then we shall have forty wet days. How disgusting!'

'Get into bed, all of you!' said Mother, coming in unexpectedly. 'Quick! The storm will soon be over.'

It lasted about half an hour, and then the children could hear only distant rumblings; but the rain went on and on. They all fell asleep again, and Pat awoke later on. He switched on his light to see the time.

'Three minutes to twelve. Oh – I wonder if it is still raining!' he said. He jumped out of bed and ran to the window. There was a drip-drip-drip to be heard – but it wasn't the rain, only the drops falling from leaf to leaf. The sky had cleared and was now full of stars instead of clouds. Pat was delighted. 'That storm spent itself just in time,' he thought, jumping back into bed. 'The others will be glad.'

Next day was very hot indeed, but everywhere was moist and damp. The steam arose from fences and grass, trees and walls. It was queer to see it. Uncle Merry called from the next garden.

'You'll have to put on thick shoes for our walk. We had a terrific downpour in the night, and it will be soaking underfoot.'

'But it wasn't raining at midnight,' said Pat. 'So if it doesn't rain any more today, we'll have a lovely summer, Uncle Merry.'

They set off in their thickest shoes, but with no socks or stockings, for the day was really hot. Fergus pattered along happily, getting his short legs very wet indeed. But he never minded a little thing like that.

'Uncle Merry, *the* flower for July is the heather, isn't it?' said Janet, as they came out on the common, and saw the glorious stretch of purple before them.

'Oh, isn't it simply marvellous?'

It really was. The heather, or ling, covered the common and the distant hillside with rich colour. Here and there the children saw patches of crimson bell heather, adding its bright colour to the common. Bees were busy there by the thousand, humming contentedly.

'Heather honey is most delicious, isn't it?' said John, watching the bees visiting flower after flower. 'Uncle, even when we've walked for miles over commons we see bees there. Their hives must be a long way away.'

'They sometimes are,' said Uncle Merry. 'But a bee doesn't mind flying for many miles in order to collect the rich sweet honey that the heather has to offer him. Pick a bit of ordinary heather, or ling, John, and have a look at it. You will see that instead of the sepals being green, as those of most flowers are, they are rosy like the petals.'

'I never noticed that before,' said John, and all the

children examined the rosy-purple sepals and petals of the ling. 'I like the bell heather very much too,' said Pat, picking a spray for a button-hole. 'I love the crimson bells. Is there any other kind of heather to be found on our common, Uncle, besides the ordinary heather and the bell heather?'

'Yes, if you look about you will find a third kind,' said Uncle Merry. 'It is called the cross-leaved heath, and it has four leaves set at intervals up the stem.'

All the children hunted about, and Janet found the first piece. She put some in her button-hole. 'There must be about a million bees on the common today,' she said, waving away two that were flying after her button-hole.

'It must be fun to be a bee,' said John, 'to go out every day and hunt for honey – and to take pollen to all the different flowers – and to go home and tell all the others your news. I like bees.'

'So do I, but I don't like wasps,' said Janet. 'They are such a nuisance when the fruit begins to ripen, and they do worry us so when we have summer picnics. I shouldn't think wasps are any use to us at all, are they, Uncle Merry?'

'They are in the early summer, when they have thousands of young grubs to feed,' said Uncle Merry. 'For they like to take flies and small insects to their grubs. Haven't you seen them chasing houseflies up the windowpane, catching them, nipping off their wings and flying away with the bodies?'

'Yes, *I* have,' said John, 'and once I saw a wasp catch a butterfly and try to bite off *his* wings, Uncle.'

'They are clever little creatures,' said Uncle Merry, 'and they make wonderful papery nests.'

The ramblers walked on over the heath, enjoying the heather. A bird began to sing somewhere, and John pricked up his ears.

'Uncle Merry, what is that bird? It's about the only one I've heard singing lately. All the others seem to be silent now – even the cuckoo who sang all day long in May and June.'

They stood and listened to the little bird and then they saw him. He flew from a bush, yellow in the sunshine.

'There he is!' said Uncle Merry. 'The yellowhammer. His song is one of the oftenest heard in the summertime. Listen – he says, "Little bit of bread and NO cheese! Little bit of bread and NO cheese!"'

'Oh – it really does sound exactly as if he's saying that!' cried Janet, pleased. And it did. The children always knew the yellowhammer's voice after that, and sometimes sang his queer little song with him. It was very plainly to be heard, for there was little other bird song in July.

The sky was full of swallows, martins and swifts, soaring and swooping all day long. The children had seen the martins' nests under the eaves of some cottages down their lane, and had eagerly watched the parent birds bringing thousands of flies to the little ones. Some of the little martins had already flown, and were soaring through the sky with their parents.

'When do they leave us?' asked John. 'I do hope they won't go for a long time. I love the swallows and the martins.'

'They will go in September and October,' said Uncle Merry, 'but the swifts will leave next month. Some of the old cuckoos will leave us this month, towards the end.'

'Oh dear,' sighed Janet. 'I don't like to think of our migrants going yet. It seems as if they've only just come. Why does the summer go so quickly, Uncle Merry, and the winter go so slowly?'

They left the common and came into a dim green lane, heavily overshadowed by big elm trees that met overhead. It was very damp underfoot, for the trees had dripped all night long. The ditches were moist too.

The children stopped in amazement halfway down the lane. 'Uncle – look!' said Janet. 'Little frogs – hundreds of them!'

'It must have been raining frogs!' said Pat, with an astonished laugh.

It was indeed a queer sight, for on every side, hop-hop-hopping, were the small frogs. The children stood and watched them.

'I'm glad we saw this,' said Uncle Merry. 'It is part of the story of the frog-spawn and the tadpoles. These tiny frogs were the tadpoles we saw in May. Now they have grown their legs. They can breathe the air properly, and their tails have disappeared. They are baby frogs, who in five years' time will be grown-up frogs.'

'But, Uncle, why are they all here in such numbers?' asked Pat, watching a little crowd of them making for the damp, rain-wet ditch.

'Well,' said his uncle, 'there comes a time when all sensible frogs must leave their pond-life and live a land-life. They must find homes for themselves in damp ditches, water-meadows, and wet banks; and naturally they choose a day when the ground is wet, because they don't like anywhere dry.'

'And of course after that storm last night, everywhere is beautifully damp for them,' said Pat; 'so I suppose each little frog had the same good idea, Uncle, and said, "Off we go!"'

'Quite right,' said Uncle Merry. 'It's an amusing sight, isn't it? In years gone by, country folk used to say it had been raining frogs when they saw this crowd of tiny frogs, and they really believed that it *had* been raining frogs.'

Fergus was most interested in the little frogs, but he didn't like their sudden jumps and jerks, so he left them alone. The children made their way down the damp lane, trying not to tread on any of the journeying frogs. They really were funny little things.

They came to the fields, and began to look about for new flowers. They had already found and named dozens of the ones around them. Uncle Merry smiled to hear them talk.

'That's not new – that's tormentil. And there is red

campion again – and ragged robin in the ditch. There's a white campion. I like the red ones best.'

'Here's another campion!' said John suddenly. 'New flower, Uncle! I saw it in my book the other day, but I've forgotten its name.'

'Well, it's easy to remember,' said Uncle Merry, taking the flower from him. 'Look at this blown-out sepal-cup behind the petals – just like a little bladder.'

'Oh *yes*,' said John, 'it's bladder campion, of course! How silly of me!'

Janet brought him two yellow flowers, each with five petals opening out like tiny yellow wild roses. One plant had beautiful five-fingered leaves, pretty to see. The other had quite different leaves, silvery underneath.

'Ah, Janet, I'm glad you've brought me these two flowers together,' said Uncle Merry. 'We can see why they get their names, and what is the difference between them. This one, with five-fingered leaves, is the cinquefoil. Cinque means five, as you know, and foil means leaf, so its name is really five-leaf. The other has silvery leaves – see the underside of them. So we call it silverweed. You'll easily remember these two little yellow plants now, won't you?'

'Oh yes,' said Janet. 'Cinquefoil or five-leaf, and silverweed. Pat, it's your turn to bring a new flower.'

'Well, here's one,' said Pat, bringing a flower to Uncle Merry. It had small spikes of close-set pink flowers. 'There's a lot of this about everywhere, Uncle, and some of it has whitish or greenish flowers, not pink like this.'

'This is persicaria,' said Uncle Merry. 'You will find a great deal of it now. I've far too much of it in my vegetable garden. If you want a job, Pat, come along in some time and find and pull up every bit of persicaria choking my vegetables.'

'I will,' promised Pat. 'Uncle, look, are those green strings the flowers of the stinging-nettle? I've never seen them before.'

Pat tried to pick a stinging-nettle to look closely at

the green flowers, but he took his hand away quickly. 'It's stung me,' he said. 'Oh, it does smart!'

'Get a cool dock leaf,' said Uncle Merry. 'That will soothe the smart. Yes, Pat, those green threads are the nettle flowers – but, like the dog's mercury, the male and female flowers are on different plants. There is a Mr Nettle and a Mrs Nettle.'

'What makes the sting?' asked Pat, wrapping a cool dock leaf round his hand.

'Do you see those hairs on the leaves?' said Uncle Merry. 'Well, the tips are brittle, and when you touch them, they break off, pierce your skin and inject a most irritating fluid that makes your skin sting badly. As you can guess, most creatures leave stinging-nettles alone, and they spread everywhere with the greatest ease.'

'Oh, look!' cried Janet, in delight. 'Here is a bird's foot trefoil, Uncle – with its seed pods. Do you remember that you said we must look out for them when the flower had gone, and then we should see that the pod-clusters were just like a bird's foot? And so they are!'

'Another well-named plant!' said Pat, in pleasure, looking at the bird-like claw made by the bird's foot trefoil seed pods.

Soon they had to turn home, carrying their 'new' flowers with them. Janet made a face as she tried to avoid brushing her bare legs against plants scattered with little balls of frothy spit.

'Uncle, I do hate this spit-stuff,' said Janet in disgust. 'What is it? It's everywhere. Where does it come from? I don't like it.'

'It's the home of a little insect,' said Uncle Merry, laughing at Janet's disgusted face. 'Look – I'll show you.' He picked a grass with the 'spit-stuff' on it, and with his finger parted the frothy spit. In the middle of it was a small green fat insect.

'Here we are!' said Uncle Merry, showing the children the little creature. 'He doesn't like the very hot rays of the sun, so he exudes this froth to protect himself, and lives inside it. He is the grub of the frog-hopper, that nice little brown insect that hops on to your hand and then hops off again like a very tiny frog.'

'Oh yes, I know them,' said John. 'When you touch them they leap right into the air, just like frogs. Frog-hopper – what a good name; and this is where he lives before he becomes a proper brown frog-hopper, Uncle! Well, I never guessed before that frog-hopper grubs lived inside these spits, looking so cool and green.'

'We call them cuckoo-spits,' said Uncle Merry, waving his hand towards the many dozens of froth-balls on the grasses all around. 'I suppose people once thought the cuckoo made them, though I can't imagine why. John, what are you doing?'

'Just collecting a few spits to take home,' said John. 'I want to see how the grub turns into a nice brown frog-hopper that doesn't mind the sun.'

Everyone laughed. John had a great collection of

grubs and caterpillars and looked after them very well. Uncle Merry said that one day he would make a discovery that no one had made before, and John was always hoping that he would.

'It hasn't rained yet,' said Janet, looking up into the sky. 'Do you think it will, Uncle?'

'No,' said Uncle Merry. 'I feel sure it won't, so we are safe for forty days! We'll be sure to have a fine day for our next July walk, so that's good!'

'It will soon be holidays,' said Pat. 'Then we can come any day with you, Uncle; we don't need to wait for the weekends.'

'Good,' said Uncle Merry. 'We'll go the day after you break up, then. Don't forget!'

The Enchanted Sea

The Enchanted Sea

ONE LOVELY sunny morning John and Lucy went out to play in their garden. It was a very big one, and at the end was a broad field.

'Let's go and play in the field this morning!' said Lucy. So down the garden they ran and opened the gate in the wall, meaning to run out into the green field.

But oh, what a surprise! There was no field there! Instead there was the blue sea – and how Lucy and John stared and stared!

'Lucy! What's happened?' asked John, rubbing his eyes. 'Yesterday our field was here. Today there's a big sea!'

'We must be dreaming,' said Lucy. 'Let's pinch each other, John, and if we each feel the pinch, we'll know we're not dreaming.'

So they each pinched one another hard.

'Ooh!' they both cried. 'Stop! You're hurting!'

'It's not a dream, it's real,' said John, rubbing his arm. 'But oh, Lucy! It must be magic or something. Let's go and tell Mummy.'

They were just going to run back to the house when Lucy pointed to something on the smooth blue water.

'Look!' she said. 'There's a boat coming – but isn't it a funny one!'

John looked. Yes, sure enough, it was a boat – a very strange one. It had high pointed ends, and at one end was a cat's head in wood and at the other a dog's head. A yellow sail billowed out in the wind.

'Who's in the boat?' said John. 'It looks to me like a brownie or gnome, Lucy.'

'I feel a bit frightened,' said Lucy. 'Let's hide

behind our garden wall, John, and peep over the top where the pear tree is.'

They ran behind the wall, climbed the pear tree and then, hidden in its leafy branches, peeped over the top. They saw the boat come nearer and nearer, and at last it reached the shore. Out jumped the brownie, threw a rope round a wooden post nearby, and then ran off into the wood to the left of the children's garden.

'Well, that was one of the fairy folk for certain!' said John, in excitement. 'Did you see his pointed hat and shoes and his long beard, Lucy?'

For a long time the children watched, but the little brownie did not come back. After a bit John began to long to see the boat more closely, so he and Lucy climbed down the pear tree and ran quietly over the grass to where the boat lay rocking gently.

'Oh, Lucy, it must be a magic one!' said John. 'Do let's get in it just for a moment to see what it feels like! Think how grand it will be to tell everyone we have sat in a brownie's boat!'

So the two children clambered into the little boat and sat down on the wooden seat in the middle. And then a dreadful thing happened!

The rope round the post suddenly uncoiled itself and slipped into the boat. The wind blew hard and the yellow sail billowed out. The boat rocked from end to end, and off it went over the strange enchanted sea!

'Ooh!' said Lucy, frightened. 'John! What shall we do? The boat's sailing away with us!'

But John could do nothing. The wind blew them steadily over the water, and their garden wall grew smaller and smaller, the farther away they sailed.

'That brownie will be cross to find his boat gone,' said Lucy, almost crying. 'Where do you suppose it's taking us?'

On and on went the little boat, the dog's head pointing forwards and the cat's head backwards. Lucy looked at the back of the dog's head, and thought that it looked a little like their dog at home.

'I do wish we had our dear Rover with us,' she said.

'I'm sure he would be a great help.'

To her great surprise the wooden dog's head pricked up its ears and the head turned round and looked at her.

'If you are fond of dogs, I shall be pleased to help you,' it said.

'You did give us a fright!' said John, almost falling off his seat in surprise. 'Are you magic?'

'Yes, and so is the wooden cat over there,' said the dog. 'We're only wooden figureheads, but there's plenty of good magic about us. You look nice little children, and if you are fond of animals and kind to them, the cat and I will be very glad to help you.'

'Meeow!' said the cat's head, and it turned round and smiled at the two astonished children.

'Well, first of all, can you tell us about this strange sea?' asked John. 'It's never been here before.'

'Oh yes, it has, but usually at night-time when nobody is about to see it,' said the dog. 'It belongs to the Wizard High-Hat. He sent his servant, the brownie Tick-a-tock, to fetch a red-and-yellow toadstool from the wood near your garden and made the sea stretch from his island to there, so that Tick-a-tock could sail quickly there and back.'

'But I expect he lay down and fell asleep,' said the cat. 'He's always doing that. So when you got into the boat, it sailed off with you instead of the brownie. It doesn't know the difference between you, you see.'

'Oh goodness!' said John, in a fright. 'Does that mean it's taking us to the Wizard High-Hat?'

'Yes,' said the dog, 'and he'll be in a fine temper when he sees you instead of the brownie!'

'Whatever shall we do?' said Lucy, looking anxiously round to see if the wizard's island was anywhere in sight.

'Well, we might be able to help you, if you'll just say a spell over us to make us come properly alive when we get to the island,' said the dog. 'If we were a proper dog and cat we could perhaps protect you.'

'What is the spell?' asked John.

'One of you must stroke my head, and the other must pat the cat's head,' said the dog, looking quite excited. The cat mewed loudly and blinked her green eyes. 'Then you must say the magic word I'll whisper into your ear, and stamp seven times on the bottom of the boat. Then you'll see what happens when we reach the shore. Don't do any of these things till we reach the island.'

The dog whispered the magic word into each child's ear, and they repeated it again and again to themselves to make sure they had it right. Then suddenly Lucy pointed in front of the boat.

'Look!' she said. 'There's the island – and, oh my! Is that the wizard's palace on that hill in the middle?'

'Yes,' said the dog. 'You'll see some of his soldiers in a minute. They always meet the boat.'

Sure enough the children saw six little soldiers come marching out of the palace gates towards the shore. They were dressed in red, and looked very like John's wooden soldiers at home.

The boat sailed nearer and nearer to the shore, and the dog told John and Lucy to use the spell he had taught them. So John stroked the dog's head, Lucy patted the cat's head, and each of them said the magic word, and then stamped loudly on the bottom of the boat seven times.

And what a surprise they had! Each wooden head grew legs and a body, and hey presto, a live cat and dog jumped down from the ends of the boat and frisked round the children in delight!

'We're real, we're real!' they cried. 'Now we can go with you and help you.'

The boat grounded on the sandy shore and the rope flew out and tied itself round a post. The chief of the soldiers stepped up and looked most astonished to see the two children.

'Where's Tick-a-tock the brownie?' he asked, sternly. 'What are you doing here?'

'Well, you see, we stepped into the brownie's

boat and it sailed off with us,' said John. 'We're very sorry, and please would you ask the wizard to excuse us and send the boat back to our garden to take us home again?'

'You must come and ask him yourself,' said the soldier. 'You are very naughty children!'

The six soldiers surrounded John and Lucy and marched them off towards the palace on the hill. The dog and cat followed behind, and the soldiers took no notice of them.

Soon the children were mounting the long flight of steps up to the castle, and were pushed into a large hall, where sat the Wizard High-Hat on a silver throne. He looked most surprised when he saw John and Lucy, and at once demanded to know how they got there.

John told him, and he frowned.

'Now that is most annoying,' he said crossly. 'I want to send my sea to another place tomorrow, and that means that Tick-a-tock won't get back with the toadstool. I shall keep you prisoner here for a hundred years, unless you can do the things I tell you to do.'

Lucy began to cry, and John turned pale.

'Please don't set us very hard tasks,' he said. 'I'm only eight years old, and Lucy's only seven, and doesn't know her six times table yet.'

The wizard laughed scornfully, and commanded his soldiers to take the children to the bead-room. They were led to a small room with a tiny window set high up. On the floor were thousands and thousands of beads of all colours and sizes.

'Now,' said the wizard, 'your first task is to sort out all these beads into their different colours and sizes. You can have today and tonight to do this in, and if you haven't finished by tomorrow morning you shall be my prisoners for a hundred years.'

With that he closed the door with a bang, and he and his soldiers tramped away. The children looked at one another in dismay.

'We can never do that!' said Lucy, in despair. 'Why,

it would take us weeks to sort out all these beads!'

'Where are the cat and dog?' asked John, looking all round. 'They don't seem to be here. They might have helped us.'

Suddenly the door opened again, and the dog and cat were flung into the room, panting. Then the door closed again, and the four were prisoners.

'We thought we wouldn't be able to get to you!' said the dog. 'So I bit a soldier on the leg and the cat scratched another on the hand, and they were so angry that they threw us in here with you!'

'Just see what we've got to do!' said Lucy, in despair, and she pointed to the beads. 'We've got to sort out all these before tomorrow morning.'

'My word!' said the dog, blowing out his whiskered cheeks. 'That's a dreadful job! Come, Puss! Let's all set to work.'

The four began to sort out the beads, and for an hour they worked steadily. Then the door opened and a soldier put a loaf of bread, a bone, a jug of water and a saucer of milk into the room. Then the door shut and the key was turned.

The children ate the bread and drank the water. The dog gnawed the bone and the cat drank the milk.

'It's no use going on with these beads,' said the cat, suddenly. 'We shall never get them done. I know what I'll do!'

'What?' asked the children, excitedly.

'You wait and see!' said the cat, and she finished her milk. Then she washed herself. After that she went round the little room, and looked very hard at every hole in the wall.

'Now watch!' she said. She sat down in the middle of the floor and began to make a curious squeaking noise that sounded like a thousand mice squealing at once – and a very curious thing happened!

Out of the mouse holes round the room there came running hundreds of little brown mice. They scampered to where the cat sat, and made ring after ring round her. When about a thousand mice were there, the cat stopped making the curious noise and glared at the mice.

'I could eat you all!' she said, in a frightening voice. 'But if you will do something for me, I will set you free!'

She pointed to the beads. 'Sort those out into their different colours and sizes!' she said. 'And be quick about it!'

At once the thousand mice scuttled to the beads. Each mouse chose a bead of a certain colour and size and carefully put it to start a pile. Soon the little piles grew and grew, and the big pile sank to nothing. In half an hour all the thousands of beads were neatly sorted out into hundreds of piles of beads, all of different colours and sizes.

'Good!' said the cat to the trembling mice. 'You may go!'

Off scampered the mice to their holes and disappeared. The children hugged the clever cat, and thanked her.

'Now we'll let the wizard know his task is done!' said the cat. 'Kick the door, John.'

John kicked the door and an angry soldier opened it.

'Tell the wizard we've finished our work,' said John, and the soldier gaped in astonishment to see the neat piles of beads. He fetched the wizard, who could hardly believe his eyes.

'Take them to the Long Field!' said High-Hat to his soldiers. So the children, followed by the cat and dog, were taken to a great field which was surrounded on all sides by high fences. The grass in this field was very long, almost up to the children's knees.

'Here is a pair of scissors for each of you,' said the wizard, with a cunning smile. 'Cut this grass for me before morning, or I will keep you prisoner for a hundred years!'

The children looked at the scissors in dismay. They were very small, and the grass was so long and there was such a lot of it! The wizard and his soldiers shut the gate of the field and left the four alone together.

'Well, I don't know what we're going to do this time' said John, beginning to cut the grass with his scissors, 'but it seems to me we're beaten!'

He and Lucy cut away for about an hour, but at the end of that time their hands were so tired, and they had cut so small a patch of grass that they knew it was of no use going on. They would never get even a tenth of the field cut by the morning.

'Can't you think of something clever to help us again?' asked John at last, turning to the cat and dog.

'We're both thinking hard,' said the cat. 'I believe the dog has an idea. Don't disturb him for a minute.'

The dog was lying down, frowning. Lucy and John kept very quiet. Suddenly the dog jumped up and ran to Lucy.

'Feel round my collar,' he said to her. 'You'll find a little wooden whistle there.'

Lucy soon found the whistle, and the dog put it

into his mouth. Then he began to whistle very softly. The sound was like the wind in the grass, the drone of bees and the tinkling of faraway water.

Suddenly, holes appeared in the earth all around the high fence, and hundreds of grey rabbits peeped out of them. They had dug their way into the field under the fence, and as soon as they saw the dog blowing on his magic whistle, they ran up to him and sat down in rings round him. He took the whistle from his mouth and looked at them.

'I chase rabbits!' he said. 'But I will let you go free if you will do something for me. Do you see this beautiful green juicy grass? Eat it as quickly as you can, and you shall go the way you came.'

At once the rabbits set to work nibbling the green grass. It was very delicious and they enjoyed it. In an hour's time the whole field was as smooth as velvet, and not a blade of grass was longer than Lucy's little finger.

'Good!' said the dog to the rabbits. 'You may go!'

At once they scampered away. John ran to the gate in the fence and hammered on it. The wizard himself opened it, and when he saw the smooth field, with all the long grass gone, he gasped in astonishment.

'Where's the grass you cut?' he asked at last, looking here and there.

The children didn't know what to say, so they didn't answer. The wizard grew angry, and called his soldiers.

'Take them to the topmost room of my palace and lock them in!' he roared. 'They have been using magic! Well, they'll find themselves somewhere they can't use magic now!'

In half a minute the soldiers surrounded the children and animals again and hustled them back to the palace. Up hundreds and hundreds of stairs they took them, and at last, right at the very top, they came to a room that was locked. The wizard took a key from his girdle and unlocked the door. The children and animals were pushed inside and the door was locked on the outside.

By this time it was almost night-time. A tiny lamp burnt high up in the ceiling. There was one window, but it was barred across. John looked round in despair.

'Well, I don't see what we can do now!' he said, with a sigh. 'I'm afraid, cat and dog, that even you, clever though you are, can't do anything to help us.'

The dog and cat prowled all round the room, but the walls were strong and thick, and the door was locked fast. For a long time the four sat on the floor together, then suddenly the cat jumped up and ran to the window.

'Open it!' she said. 'I want to see if I can squeeze through the bars.'

Lucy and John opened the heavy window, and the cat jumped lightly on to the ledge.

'What's the good of squeezing through the bars?' asked John, peering down. 'You could never jump down, Puss! Why, we're right at the very top of the palace!'

The cat squeezed through the bars and stood

on the outer window ledge. Her green eyes shone in the darkness.

'There's another window ledge nearby!' she whispered. 'I will jump on to that, and see if the window there is open. If it is, I'll go in, and see if I can find some ways of helping you all to escape!'

With that she jumped neatly to the next window ledge, and disappeared. The window there was open and the brave cat leapt lightly into the room. The palace was in darkness. Wizard, soldiers and servants were all sleeping. The soft-footed cat ran down the stairs, and at last reached a room from which loud snores came. She ran in, and by the light of a small candle saw the wizard asleep on his bed. On the table near the candle lay his keys!

In a trice the cat had them in her mouth and back she went up the stairs, leapt on to the window ledge, and then jumped on to the next ledge, mewing to the children as she jumped. How excited they were to see the keys!

John fitted them one by one into the lock of the door until he found the right one. He turned it, and the door opened! Quietly the two children, the cat and the dog slipped down the hundreds of stairs and undid the heavy palace door. Out they went into the moonlight, and ran down to the seashore.

'I do hope the sea still stretches to our garden wall,' said John. 'Hurry up, little boat, and take us home again.'

The boat set off over the water. Suddenly Lucy gave a cry and pointed to each end of the boat. The dog and cat had disappeared, and once more the two wooden figure-heads stood high at each end.

'The magic is gone from them!' said Lucy. 'Oh, I do hope they don't mind. They're gone back to wooden heads again.'

'Don't worry about us,' said the dog. 'We've enjoyed our adventure, and we're quite happy. I only hope the boat will take you home again.'

On and on sailed the little ship in the bright

moonlight. After a long time John caught Lucy's arm and pointed.

'Our garden wall!' he said, in delight.

'Who's that on the edge of the sea?' asked Lucy, seeing a little figure standing there.

'It must be Tick-a-tock the brownie!' said John. 'How pleased he will be to see his boat coming back again. I expect he thought he was quite lost.'

The boat touched the grass, and the children jumped out. They called goodbye to the dog and cat, and then felt themselves pushed aside. The brownie had rushed up to his boat, and leapt in as quickly as he could. The sails filled out and off went the boat in the moonlight, the dog barking and the cat mewing in farewell.

'That's the end of a most exciting adventure,' said John. 'Goodness, I wonder what Mummy has been thinking all this time! We'll tell her all about our adventure, and in the morning perhaps Daddy will make us a raft and we can all go exploring on the magic sea.'

Mummy was glad to see them. She had been so worried. She could hardly believe her ears when she heard all that had happened.

'You must go to bed now,' she said. 'But tomorrow we'll all go down to see the enchanted water, and perhaps Daddy will sail off to the wizard's island to punish him for keeping you prisoner.'

But in the morning the sea was gone! Not a single sign of it was left – there were only green fields and hills stretching far away into the distance. The wizard had called his sea back again, and although John and Lucy have watched for it to return every single day, it never has. Isn't it a pity?

A Knot in
Twiddle's Hanky

A Knot in
Twiddle's Hanky

'I DO wish I could remember things,' said Mr Twiddle in despair. 'I meant to go and fetch my shoes before the shops closed, so that I could go for a nice walk this evening – and I forgot.'

'And you can't possibly go for a walk in those old shoes you're wearing,' said Mrs Twiddle. 'Why don't you tie a knot in your hanky, or something, Twiddle, then you would see it and remember you had to do something?'

'Well, that's just what I *will* do!' said Mr Twiddle, and he took out his big red handkerchief and tied a large knot at one corner. 'There! Now, when I see that knot I shall know I must remember something.'

'What are you going to remember?' asked Mrs Twiddle, with a little squeal of laughter.

'Oh, dear me, yes – I forgot I had to have something to remember, before I tied a knot,' said Mr Twiddle. 'Well, I know – I really must remember to fetch my shoes tomorrow. I'll leave the knot in for that.'

So he left it in, and went to read his paper in the garden. Before very long he took out his red hanky to mop his head – and he saw the knot.

'Aha! The knot! Now that was to make sure I remembered something. What was it?'

But for the life of him poor Mr Twiddle couldn't remember what the knot was for! So he called his wife. 'Wife, can you think of anything I said I would do, and haven't done?' he asked.

'Good gracious, yes!' said Mrs Twiddle at once, thinking of a whole lot of things. 'What about cutting the grass?'

'Oh, dear – did I really put the knot in my hanky for that?' said Mr Twiddle, with a sigh. 'Well, well – it's no good putting knots in if I don't take any notice of them.' So he got up, fetched the mowing machine and began to cut the grass.

He was so hot when he had finished that he sat down on the seat to rest. He pulled out his hanky – and in it he saw the knot again. He had forgotten to undo it! So he thought it was another knot, of course. He stared at it, frowning.

'Good gracious! Now what's *this* knot for?' he wondered. He called to his wife. 'Is there anything else I ought to do?'

'Dear me, yes! What about weeding the lettuces?' called back his wife, giggling to herself to think that dear old Twiddle hadn't undone the knot.

Twiddle got up. 'Well, I never! Was that what the knot was for in my hanky? What a memory I've got, to be sure.'

So off he went to weed the lettuce bed, and it took

him till supper time. He was really very tired when he went in.

After his supper he took out his hanky to wipe some crumbs off his waistcoat – and again he saw the very same knot.

'Look at that!' he said to his wife, who turned away to laugh all by herself. 'What's *that* knot for, I'd like to know?'

'You haven't filled the coal bucket for me,' said Mrs Twiddle. 'Would it be that, Twiddle?'

'It might be,' said Twiddle. 'Anyway, I'll do it. Oh, dear, what a pity I saw the knot!'

He saw it again just before he went to bed. 'Bless us all! Here's a knot in my hanky again!' he said to his wife. 'The things I have to remember! What can it be now? Is there anything important I must do?'

'Yes. Put the cat out, and then get her in again,' said Mrs Twiddle, lighting her candle to go up to bed. 'You always forget that, Twiddle.'

Twiddle groaned. 'That cat! I let her in and out all

day long. She just does it on purpose. And yet at night, when I kindly open the door for her without her asking me, she won't go out. Puss, come along! Out you go!'

Mrs Twiddle had gone upstairs by the time Mr Twiddle had let the cat out and waited patiently for it to come back again. He went up with his candle and got into bed beside his plump little wife.

He took his hanky to put under the pillow – and dear me, he saw the knot again! Yes, the very same knot!

Mrs Twiddle was asleep. Twiddle couldn't bear to waken her. He stared at the knot and tried to puzzle out what it was there to remind him of. To fasten all the windows? To rake out the kitchen fire? To see if the larder door was safely shut? To – to – to – well, what *was* the knot for?

Poor Twiddle got out of bed, put on his dressing gown and went downstairs to see if he could find something he had forgotten to do. But he couldn't.

The doors were locked, the windows were fastened, the larder was shut, the fire was raked out. Then what could it be?

He went into the sitting-room to see if everything was all right there, and fell over the cat, which got between his legs in her usual annoying way. He fell down with a crash, knocked over a little table, and down went Mrs Twiddle's pet fern!

Mrs Twiddle woke up with a dreadful jump. 'Twiddle!' she said sharply. 'Burglars! Quick, Twiddle!'

But Twiddle wasn't there. Mrs Twiddle put on her dressing gown and went downstairs in time to see Twiddle pelting the cat with the earth out of her plant pot! She was very cross indeed.

'Really, Twiddle! Have you *got* to do this sort of thing in the middle of the night when I'm sound asleep? The poor cat! And my poor fern! Puss, Puss, come to me, then. Naughty Twiddle, what was he doing to you?'

'*Well!*' said Twiddle, annoyed. 'I like *that*! Why don't you ask your cat what she was doing to *me*? Tripping me up on purpose!'

'What did you come down for?' asked Mrs Twiddle, crossly.

'Well – to see if I'd forgotten to do something,' said Twiddle. 'But everything seems all right. I'm coming to bed. But that cat isn't, wife. Leave her in the kitchen, please.'

'Poor Pussy!' said Mrs Twiddle, and put the cat down. They went up to bed together and took off their dressing gowns. Just as he got into bed, Twiddle saw his hanky on the pillow and stared at the knot.

'That knot again!' he cried. 'What's it to remind me of *now*, I'd like to know. I'll never put another knot in my hanky again!'

'You won't need to!' said Mrs Twiddle, with a laugh. 'You seem to keep the same one in all the time. You never undo it! Oh, Twiddle, you'll be the death of me one day, with your foolish ways. Now, you listen to me – that knot is to tell you to lie down, shut your eyes and go to sleep!'

'Is it really?' said Twiddle, blowing out his candle and lying down very thankfully. 'Well, well, well – to think I put a knot in my hanky to remind me to do something I could *never* forget to do!'

And off he went to sleep. But I wonder if he'll remember to fetch his shoes next day? Do you think he will?

The Fox and
the Six Cats

The Fox and
the Six Cats

THERE WERE once six cats who all belonged to an old lady called Miss Two-Shoes. There was a brown cat, a black cat, a white one, a ginger one, a tabby one, and one that was every colour mixed.

Every day for their dinner Miss Two-Shoes put out six dishes of boiled fish and milk. The cats loved fish, and ate their dinners hungrily, always wishing for more.

'If only we knew where these fish came from, we might be able to go and get some,' said the black cat, cleaning her whiskers carefully.

'*I* know where they live!' said the ginger cat. 'They

live in the river that runs in the field at the bottom of our garden! Last night, when I was prowling about there, I saw a man with a long rod and line. He threw the line into the river, and very soon, when he pulled it out again, there was a wriggling fish on the end.'

'Ho!' said the white cat, yawning widely. 'So that's where the fish come from, is it? Well, I don't see how we can catch any, unless we have a rod and line ourselves!'

All the cats had listened to what the ginger cat had said, and each had made up his mind that he would go that night, all by himself, and watch the fisherman at work.

So when night fell, all the cats started off for the river, and none of them saw each other, for they trod so quietly on their velvet paws.

The fisherman was there. He had baited his line, and was just casting it into the wide river. Then he felt in his pocket for his pipe, for he loved to smoke whilst he was waiting in the moonlight for the fish to bite. But he had left his pipe in his cottage at the other end of the field.

'Bother!' he said crossly. 'I must either go without my smoke or walk back to my cottage. Well, I will balance my rod carefully here, and go quickly to fetch my pipe. I don't suppose any fish will bite yet.'

He put his rod down and set off to walk to his cottage; and, do you know, he had hardly taken ten steps before a big fish snapped at the bait! The hook stuck into his mouth and it was caught!

Then it began to wriggle and struggle, and the six watching cats suddenly saw it jumping in and out of the water. Each of them darted forward to take the fish, and how cross they were when they saw the others!

'Quick!' said the black cat, pouncing on the rod and holding it. 'One of you reel in the line.'

The ginger cat wound in the line and pulled the fish nearer. The white cat fetched the landing-net to catch the fish in. The tabby helped to hold it, whilst the brown cat shouted directions all the time. The sixth cat ran to each in turn, giving a paw here and a paw there. They were all as excited as could be.

The fish pulled hard. The rod bent nearly in two. The black cat found it quite difficult to hold, and was half afraid she would be pulled into the water.

The ginger cat wound the line in steadily, and the fish was pulled nearer and nearer to the bank. Then the white cat and the tabby tried to put the landing-net over it, and very soon they managed to. The fish was caught! It slipped into the net, the cats lifted it ashore, and the big fish lay shining in the moonlight.

'The fish is mine!' said the black cat. 'I held the rod!'

'No, it's mine!' said the ginger one. 'I reeled in the line!'

'Well, I fetched the landing-net!' said the white cat.

'And I helped to hold it!' said the tabby.

'I told you all what to do!' said the brown cat.

'And I helped every one in turn,' said the sixth

one. 'Besides, I'm sure I saw the fish first. It should be mine.'

Then they all began to quarrel hard, and a fox, who was passing that way, heard them, and came to see what was the matter. When he saw the big fish lying there he was pleased, and made up his mind to get it for himself.

'Now, what's the matter?' he asked. 'Come, come, do not make this noise.'

'We each of us want the fish,' said the black cat. 'We don't know who should have it.'

'Well, I will be your judge,' said the fox. 'Now, I have heard that you all have beautiful voices, and often sing to the moon. I will hear you all sing, and then whichever of you has the loveliest voice shall have the fish.'

The cats agreed, for each secretly thought that his own voice was far the best.

'Very well,' said the sly fox. 'Now I will hear you all together. Sit up straight, fix your eyes on the moon, and sing your most beautiful song to her for two minutes without stopping. Don't take your eyes from the moon or that will count a mark against you.'

The cats all sat up straight, looked up at the moon and began to caterwaul. Oh, what a fearful noise it was! The fox thought it was dreadful; but did he wait to judge the singing? Not he! All the cats were looking hard at the moon and saw nothing but that, so the artful fox quietly picked up the fish and ran off with it, chuckling to himself as he heard the ugly song behind him.

For quite three minutes the cats sang their best, and then, becoming tired, they looked down to ask the fox which of them had won. But he wasn't there! Nor was the fish!

'Oh, the scoundrel! Oh, the rascal! Oh, the scamp!' cried all the cats angrily. 'He has stolen the fish from us!'

Then, oh, dear me! The fisherman returned, and when he found six cats howling dismally, and his rod and line all disarranged, he *was* angry! He boxed all the cats' ears and sent them mewing away.

'If only we had been sensible and shared the big fish between us we should be eating it now!' said the black cat. 'How silly we are!'

And they were, weren't they?

Mister Meddle
and the Bull

Mister Meddle
and the Bull

DID YOU ever hear about Mister Meddle and the bull? It's really rather funny.

Well, one day Mister Meddle got up feeling good. 'I'd like to do a good deed today,' he thought. 'I'd like to help an old woman across the road, or carry a heavy parcel for someone, or jump into the river and save somebody from drowning. I feel good enough for all those things.'

He went out to do his shopping as usual, and he looked about for a runaway horse that he could stop. But all the horses trotted along properly and not one ran away. So that was no good.

Then he walked by the river to see if anyone would fall in so that he could rescue them. But nobody did.

Then he looked about for anyone carrying a heavy parcel, but the only person he saw was Mr Grumps, so he pretended not to notice he was carrying anything at all.

He waited about to see if any old ladies wanted to be helped over the road, but all the old ladies he saw seemed quite able to run across by themselves. So that wasn't any good either.

Mister Meddle was most disappointed. He went home by the fields, and in the distance he saw Farmer Barley, and he thought he would ask him if he could help him at all. The farmer was in the next field but one, so Mister Meddle opened the gate of the nearest field and shut it behind him, meaning to walk across to see the farmer.

The farmer heard the click of the gate and turned to look over the hedge to see who it was.

'I say!' began Meddle, shouting loudly. 'Do you want...'

But Farmer Barley didn't wait to hear what Meddle said. He yelled over the hedge:

'Mind that bull!'

Meddle looked all round, but he couldn't see any bull. The farmer shouted again.

'Didn't you hear me telling you to mind that bull?'

'Now why does he want me to mind his bull?' wondered Meddle. 'Oh – I suppose he wants to go home to his dinner or something, and would like me to mind the bull for him whilst he goes. Well, as I'm looking for something good to do, I'll do what he says.'

Meddle yelled back to Farmer Barley, 'All right. I'll mind the bull! Don't worry!'

'Right!' said the farmer, and went off down the field towards his farm. Meddle still couldn't see any bull, though he looked hard.

But the bull had seen him! It was in a little cluster

of trees, and it didn't like the look of Meddle at all!

Meddle suddenly saw the bull looking at him. He decided that it didn't look a very kind animal.

'In fact, it looks rather fierce,' thought Meddle. 'Well, I'll mind it for the farmer, but I hope it won't try to run away or anything, because I should just hate to try and bring it back.'

The bull glared at Meddle and snorted down its nose.

'You needn't do that at me,' said Meddle to the bull. 'That's a rude noise to make at anyone minding you. Don't worry. I shan't come any nearer to you. I shall stay here and you can stay there.'

But the bull didn't think the same as Meddle! It came out of the trees with a run and snorted at Meddle again, whisking its big tail up into the air.

'I wonder if bulls are pleased when they wag their tails,' thought Meddle, feeling rather uncomfortable. 'Dogs are, I know – but this bull doesn't look at all pleased as he wags his tail. Not one bit pleased. In fact, he looks awfully angry.'

Meddle moved away a bit. The bull moved a little nearer and gave such an alarming snort that Meddle almost jumped out of his skin.

'You're making it very difficult for me to mind you!' he shouted to the bull. 'Do behave yourself. I'm only minding you till the farmer comes back.'

The bull made up his mind that he couldn't bear Meddle in his field one minute longer. So he snorted again and ran headlong at him, putting his head down in a horrid manner. Meddle took one look at the bull's horns and fled!

How he ran! He tore to the gate with the bull after him, and got there just as the bull did. The bull tried to help him over the gate with his horns and tore Meddle's trousers, making a big hole. Meddle tumbled to the other side of the gate with a bump. The bull put his head over the top bar and snorted all over Meddle.

'You are a disgusting and most ungrateful animal,'

said Meddle angrily. 'Look what you've done to my trousers! And all because I was doing a good deed and minding you for the farmer. Well – I'm not minding you any more, so you can just do what you like! I'm going to complain about you to the farmer!'

So Meddle marched off to the farmhouse, feeling very angry indeed. He rapped on the door and the farmer opened it.

'What's the matter?' he asked.

'Plenty!' said Meddle. 'Look at my trousers – new last week, and that bull of yours chased me and tore them!'

'Well, I told you to mind him,' said the farmer. 'You should have got out of the field before he came for you.'

'Well, I thought it would be better to mind him for you in the field,' said Meddle. 'That's what comes of trying to do you a good turn.'

'What's all this about a good turn?' said the farmer, astonished. 'I didn't want you to do me a good turn!

I wanted you to get out of that field as quickly as possible before the bull turned on you. When I told you to *mind* the bull I meant you to look out that he didn't chase you!'

'Well, why didn't you say so?' said Meddle, in a rage. He turned to go and nearly fell over a fat pig.

'Mind that pig now – mind that pig!' cried the farmer.

Poor Meddle! He does get into trouble, doesn't he?

Mr Pink-Whistle's Party

Mr Pink-Whistle's Party

YOU REMEMBER Mr Pink-Whistle, don't you – the little man with pointed ears who goes about the world putting wrong things right? He is half a brownie, and can make himself invisible if he wants to.

Mr Pink-Whistle often passed a little house called Merry-Chimneys. He liked that name – and he liked the little girl who lived there.

She always seemed to be swinging on her garden gate when he passed. She smiled at him and waved cheerily. One day he stopped and spoke to her.

'What's your name? It ought to be Smiley because you're always smiling!'

The little girl laughed. 'Well, my name is *almost* as good as that,' she said. 'It's Merry.'

'Ah – Merry by name and merry by nature,' said Mr Pink-Whistle. 'Very nice. But do tell me – why are you so often out here swinging on your gate?'

'Oh, don't you know?' said the little girl. 'It's because there's a "PLEASE CROSS HERE" sign.'

Mr Pink-Whistle looked surprised. He had certainly seen the 'PLEASE CROSS HERE' sign, and had noticed the thick, white lines painted across the road, just opposite the little girl's house. But what had that got to do with swinging on a gate?

'You look puzzled!' said Merry. 'I'll explain. Well, my mother says everyone ought to do something to help other people, and if we can't see something, we've got to look for it. Mother said I'd got something right at the front gate – helping people over the busy crossing. Cars are supposed to stop, but they don't always.'

'Show me what you do,' said Mr Pink-Whistle.

'Well, look – there's a Toddlers' Home three doors away,' said Merry. 'And I'm waiting for the nurses to come out with the children, so that I can help them across the road. They have to wheel prams with four or five babies in them, so they can't very well look after the children who are walking, too. Here they come. Now watch.'

Merry skipped down from the gate and went to meet two nurses and a crowd of tiny children walking hand-in-hand in twos.

They were chattering like sparrows. The nurses had an enormous pram each with children in them. What a weight to push along!

'Hallo, Merry. There's Merry! Merry, take my hand!' called the tiny children. The nurses nodded and smiled at the little girl, and went across the crossing with their prams. Merry carefully took every small child across herself, even holding up her hand to stop a car that was coming along.

When they had all gone over safely she skipped

back to Mr Pink-Whistle. 'There you are,' she said. 'It's only a very little job, but it's a help, isn't it?'

'It certainly is,' said Mr Pink-Whistle. 'You did that well. Are you going in now you've done your job?'

'I've just got to wait for old Mr Brown and poor Mrs Smith,' said Merry. 'They come along about this time and somebody just has to help them across. They go so slowly, you see, and they are frightened of the cars. Here's Mr Brown.'

Pink-Whistle watched Merry guide the old fellow across the road. She chattered away to him, keeping a sharp eye out all the time for traffic. As soon as she got back to Pink-Whistle, along came Mrs Smith. One of her legs was much shorter than the other, and she *really* couldn't hurry.

Merry took the woman safely across and carried her basket. Then she ran back again.

'Now I'm going in,' she said. 'I always know the time to come and swing on my gate and wait for all these people. Sometimes I come out just in *case* there might be somebody else afraid to cross – when I have a minute to spare. I suppose you wouldn't like me to help you across, would you?'

'I don't have to cross just here,' said Pink-Whistle. 'But thank you all the same. I'm glad to know you, Merry. There aren't many people like you in the world.'

The next time Mr Pink-Whistle passed by Merry's house, she waved to him again. 'Mr Pink-Whistle!' she called. 'Aren't I lucky! I'm going to a big party tomorrow, and I've got a new blue dress and blue shoes to match.'

'How lovely!' said Pink-Whistle. 'Well, you deserve a party, Merry.'

'There's going to be an enormous cake with candles,' said Merry. 'And a Punch and Judy Show – fancy that! And each child is to have two balloons and a present. Aren't I *lucky*!'

'I'll come by tomorrow morning at this time and you can show me your blue shoes,' said Mr Pink-

Whistle. 'You get them out ready for me to see.'

But when he came the next day, there was no Merry swinging on the gate. He couldn't see her at all, not even at one of the windows. What could have happened?

'Perhaps she has gone shopping,' thought Pink-Whistle, and he waited a few minutes for her to come back. But she didn't. So Pink-Whistle walked up to the front door and rang the bell. A maid answered the door and Pink-Whistle asked for Merry.

'She's out in the back garden, sir,' said the little maid. 'Would you like to go and find her?'

So out into the garden went Pink-Whistle and looked all round. There was a big lawn first, then an orchard, and then a kitchen garden. He couldn't see Merry anywhere. He walked down, puzzled.

No one was on the lawn. No one was in the orchard. Was anyone in the kitchen garden? No, there was nobody there, either.

There was a little garden shed nearby, and Mr

Pink-Whistle thought he heard a noise coming from it – just a little noise. He went up and peeped in.

Yes. Merry was there – but what a different Merry! No smiles now, no merry laughter. She sat huddled up in a corner on an old sack, crying all by herself.

'What's the matter?' said Pink-Whistle, walking in and sitting down beside her.

'Oh dear – you made me jump!' said Merry, wiping her eyes and giving him a very watery smile. 'Fancy you coming and finding me here!'

'Why aren't you out swinging on your gate as usual?' asked Pink-Whistle.

'I'm not allowed to for three whole weeks,' said Merry dismally. 'You see, I had a little friend to tea yesterday – and this morning her mother came to tell my mother that she's got measles. So I'm not allowed to swing on the front gate, or talk to any other children for three weeks, in case I get it too, and give it to someone else.'

'That's very bad luck,' said Pink-Whistle. 'Very bad luck indeed. What about that party you were telling me of?'

'Well, of course, I can't possibly go to that,' said Merry, beginning to cry again. 'I'm sorry I'm so silly about it, but I just can't help feeling awfully disappointed. About my blue shoes and blue dress, you know – and not seeing the Punch and Judy Show. After all, I haven't been naughty or anything, have I? It isn't my fault.'

'It isn't – and you don't deserve such a disappointment,' said Pink-Whistle, comfortingly. 'But it just so happens that *I'm* giving a Punch and Judy party this afternoon, and *I'm* going to have an enormous cake with candles on, and there'll be balloons too – so you'll be able to come to that!'

Merry looked at him in astonishment. 'Are you *really* giving a party like that?' she said. 'But – I still won't be able to come, because I mustn't mix with other people.'

'Oh, that's all right,' said Pink-Whistle, cheerfully. 'My guests can't get measles, so you can mix with them all you like. Shall we have the party down here in the orchard?'

'*Could* we? Because I'm not allowed to go anywhere by bus or train,' said Merry, her eyes beginning to shine. 'But why can't your guests get measles? I thought anybody could get them.'

'Not *my* guests,' said Pink-Whistle, getting up. 'Well, put on your blue shoes and your blue dress this afternoon and be here at three o'clock. Don't forget.'

He went off, leaving the little girl in such a state of excitement that she danced round every tree in the orchard. What a funny, wonderful little man Mr Pink-Whistle is!

At three o'clock, dressed in her blue shoes and blue frock, with a blue ribbon in her hair, Merry ran down to the orchard. Good gracious me! What had happened to it!

Every tree was hung with streamers and shining

ornaments. Great big toadstools had sprung up from the grass for tables and seats. Twelve had grown close together to make an extra big table for the guests to sit at.

The guests were coming from every direction. But they weren't children. Oh no – Mr Pink-Whistle had chosen his other kind of friends – the pixies and elves and brownies. There they came, trooping along, all dressed in their best, too!

Mr Pink-Whistle was welcoming them all, smiling even more broadly than usual. He saw Merry and went up to her. 'You look lovely in your blue shoes and blue dress,' he said. 'I'm so glad you could come to my party. Now let me tell you who's here. This is Tiptoe – and this is Jinky – and this is Silky – and this is Jolly – and this is Heyho – dear me, I hope you'll remember all their names!'

Merry liked all the little people at once. She played games with them, ate the ice creams that kept appearing on the little mushroom tables, and drank glasses of honey-lemonade. Lovely!

The tea was simply glorious. Merry counted twelve different kinds of most extraordinary sandwiches, and twelve different kinds of cakes. There were wobbly jellies and fruit salads with ice cream on top. And oh, the cake! The cake that stood in the middle of the big table!

It shone and glittered with a hundred coloured candles, and it was decorated with silver and gold balls, pink, yellow and white icing, and all kinds of sugared flowers that could be eaten.

'See what's written on the top, Merry,' said Pink-Whistle. Merry looked and went red with pleasure.

'WELCOME TO MERRY!' was written in pink icing.

'Yes, it's *your* cake,' said Pink-Whistle. 'Made specially for you. Now – what about cutting it?'

After tea there was a Punch and Judy Show. It was much better than any show Merry had ever seen, and she laughed so much that she got a stitch.

Everyone had two balloons. 'They won't burst,' said Pink-Whistle. 'They've got just a touch of magic in them. They'll last for years.'

It was the loveliest party Merry had ever been to. At the end every guest had a present in a little shiny box. They all lined up and went to Pink-Whistle one by one.

'Thank you, Mr Pink-Whistle,' each little guest said. 'Thank you for having me to your lovely party. Goodbye!'

Merry said the same – and she gave the kind little man a sudden hug. 'You planned your party for *me*, I know you did!' she said. 'It's the nicest one I've ever been to. I love you, Mr Pink-Whistle. You go round the world putting things right – and that's what *I'm* going to do too!'

'You do it already – that's why I gave this party for you,' said Pink-Whistle. 'Well, goodbye, and I hope you'll like your present. I'll look out for you on the gate in three weeks' time!'

Merry opened her parcel when she got indoors. You will never guess what was inside! Very neatly folded, wrapped carefully in tissue paper, was – a pair of silvery wings! There was a little note tied to them.

'These can be fitted on your shoulders and used on every full-moon night. Please put away carefully when not in use.'

'What a present!' said Merry, softly, in the greatest delight. 'Wings! Wings of my own!' She shook them out gently, and looked at the calendar on the wall.

'Oh, dear – it won't be full-moon night for ten days! How can I possibly wait?'

She'll have to wait, of course – but won't she be pleased to go flying in the garden when the moon is big and round and shiny! Dear old Pink-Whistle – he does know how to make people happy, doesn't he?

Second Walk
in July

Second Walk in July

Summer Holidays

THE CHILDREN were excited when they woke up on the first day of the summer holidays. Eight summer weeks stretched before them: weeks of picnics and walks, weeks of sunshine and warmth. Lovely!

'And a nice walk with Uncle Merry to start off with,' thought Janet sleepily. 'That really will be lovely. It's funny to think we never went for proper walks before – only when we had to take messages anywhere. To think of the things we never noticed! We hardly ever saw anything last year – what dull children we were!'

'Happy holidays!' said Uncle Merry, when he saw the children in the garden. 'I shall be at work all day, but I haven't forgotten my promise. We'll go for a walk after tea – it will be nice and cool then.'

It really was very hot now. The children lay and panted under the shady trees, and Fergus lay with them, his pink tongue hanging out. He seemed as much the children's dog now as Uncle Merry's, and they loved him dearly.

It was a little cooler after tea when they all set out, Fergus still hanging out his tongue. He didn't like the weather to be too hot. 'You see, he can't take off his coat as we can,' said John seriously to Uncle Merry. 'I'd just hate to wear a fur coat in the summer like poor Fergus.'

'Aren't the trees full and dark now?' said Janet. 'They were such a bright tender green in the spring – now they are a very dark green.'

'Let's go down to the lime avenue,' said Uncle Merry. 'The limes are out now, and the bees are in them. They make such a wonderful murmuring sound.'

So they went to the little lime avenue, a pathway set between a row of common lime trees. They were flowering, and the children could see the little clusters of six or seven greenish-yellow flowers hanging down, guarded by a long, narrow bract.

'Oh, the smell!' said Janet, sniffing hard. 'A bit like honeysuckle. Oh, Uncle, isn't it lovely?'

'And hark at the bees!' said John wonderingly. 'What a noise! Uncle, there must be thousands up there among the lime blossoms.'

'There are,' said Uncle Merry. 'The bees love the sweet nectar provided by the lime blossoms. We will come here again later on and see the little round green fruits of the lime. Just stand still a moment and enjoy the scent of the lime and the murmuring of the bees in it. The spirit of summer seems to be here in this little lime avenue today.'

It was a lovely thing to do. Janet made up her mind

to bring her mother there the very next day. 'It's funny,' she thought, 'this is one of the loveliest things we've done this summer, and yet I've never heard anyone talk about it. We do miss a lot of lovely things through not knowing about them or noticing them.'

They left the limes and made their way to the fields. Janet exclaimed at the corn. 'Isn't it high, Uncle? And doesn't it make a lovely whispering sound now?'

'It's got ears, and it whispers into them,' said John. 'Oh, Uncle – look, whatever's that?'

He pointed to a curious ball-shaped nest hung in the corn-stalks, about eight or nine inches from the ground. Fergus ran forward to sniff at it, but Uncle Merry pulled him back.

'No, no, Fergus – that is too precious a thing for you to destroy! John, it's the nest of a harvest mouse – a wonderful little home!'

The children stared at the tiny nest, which was only a few inches across. It was hung between some corn-stalks, and two or three of them actually went through the nest and held it up. The nest itself was made of split leaves of corn, and of grass too.

'Uncle Merry, how *can* the tiny harvest mouse weave his nest so beautifully?' said Janet, in wonder. 'It's like a tightly woven ball. Does he live inside it?'

'The whole family live there,' said Uncle Merry, laughing. 'Yes – there may be six or seven youngsters there and the mother as well.'

'Where's the door?' asked Pat, looking for an opening.

'There isn't one,' said Uncle Merry. 'When the mouse wants to get in or out, she just pushes her way between the leaves that make up the nest and squeezes through.'

'Could we wait and see her?' said John.

'I'm afraid not,' said Uncle Merry. 'She won't come out whilst she knows we are here, and certainly not whilst she smells Fergus. Come on, Fergus – we will go, and let the little mouse breathe freely once more.'

They made their way along by the cornfield, whose

high hedges were dappled with bramble blossom, both pink and white. 'There will be lots of blackberries here in the autumn,' said Pat, looking at the delicate flowers. 'We must come this way again.'

'There's some honeysuckle,' said Janet, her eye catching sight of the yellow-pink trumpets, and her nose smelling the deliciously sweet scent. 'Do you remember how sweet the honeysuckle smelt that night when we went walking? It smelt sweeter by night than by day.'

The children found a 'new' flower in the hedge that day. 'Its flowers are a bit like those of our potatoes at home,' said John. 'What is it, Uncle Merry?'

'It's the woody nightshade, or bitter-sweet,' said Uncle Merry. 'You must have seen its bright red berries in the autumn.'

'Is it the deadly, poisonous nightshade?' asked Janet, looking at the plant with a rather scared expression.

'Oh no. That is a much rarer plant and has

bell-shaped flowers,' said Uncle Merry. 'Look, John. What family do those flowers over there belong to?'

John looked at the flat clusters, and answered at once: 'The umbrella family'.

'Right,' said Uncle Merry. 'The flowers of that family are easily recognised, aren't they? This one is fool's parsley – this is wild carrot – and that tall stout one by the stream over there is angelica. Have a look at them all and note the differences. We'll take them home and look them up carefully in our books too. It is easy to muddle them up.'

'Uncle, are those bulrushes over there?' asked Janet, as they went to the stream to pick the stout stems of angelica. 'Aren't they lovely?'

'Yes, they are magnificent,' said Uncle Merry. 'They are just coming out. Don't you love their sturdy brown heads? And look into the water. There's a "new" flower for you there too. Look at its leaves and tell me what you would name it if you were asked to christen it today.'

They all looked, and Janet answered first. 'The leaves are shaped exactly like arrow-heads. I should call it arrow-head.'

'And that's exactly what it *is* called,' said Uncle Merry, pleased. 'You are clever at names, Janet. It must have been someone like you who named our common flowers, I think.'

Janet went red with pleasure. She looked at the plant growing in the slow-moving stream, and saw that it had two sets of leaves, just as the water crowfoot had – one set was narrow, growing below the surface, and those above were glossy and arrow-shaped. The flowers were white with purple blotches.

'Arrow-head,' said Janet, bending forward to pick some. 'I shall remember that easily. Oh, *Fergus*! Uncle, he's gone headfirst into the water again. I never knew such a dog for falling into ponds and streams!'

Fergus seemed to like the water that day, for he paddled about a bit before coming out. Then, as usual, he shook himself and a shower of drops flew everywhere. He pattered after the others, pleased with himself.

'I suppose he feels nice and cool now,' said Janet. 'Now don't start shaking yourself all over me again, Fergus!'

There were a great many butterflies about that sunny day. The children knew some of them, and called out their names as they fluttered by.

'Meadow brown! Cabbage white! Red admiral! Little blue! Copper! Heath! Ringlet!'

'There's one I don't know,' said Pat, pointing to a gay and pretty red and brown butterfly.

'It's a fritillary,' said Uncle Merry, 'and look, here's a queer butterfly with curious, untidy edges to his wings.'

They looked at the rusty-red wings of the butterfly, jagged round the edges. 'It's got a mark like a comma on its lower wings,' said Pat.

'Good boy,' said Uncle Merry. 'That mark gives it its name – it's the comma butterfly!'

Then they saw a brilliant, painted lady butterfly fluttering along by itself; and then Pat made a great mistake.

He saw a bright, red-spotted insect with bluish-green front-wings and crimson hind-wings with black borders. 'There's a lovely butterfly,' he said. 'Look, it's sitting on that flower; we can see it closely. Uncle, what's that butterfly called?'

'I can't see any butterfly!' said Uncle Merry, looking straight at the red-spotted insect. Pat became quite impatient. 'Uncle, you're looking *straight* at the butterfly I mean,' he said. 'You *must* be able to see it!'

John gave a giggle. 'It isn't a butterfly. It's a moth, Pat. Don't you remember Uncle telling us that moths put their wings flat down on their backs, and that they have either feathery feelers or thread-like ones?'

Pat looked closely at the moth and felt cross with himself. 'Of course,' he said. 'It's a moth! Sorry to be so silly, Uncle Merry! I can see its thread-like feelers now. They are not knobbed, as butterflies' feelers are, and it isn't putting its wings back to back either.'

'Careless boy, aren't you?' said Uncle Merry, with a twinkle. 'Yes – it's a day-flying moth, a six-spot burnet. All the burnets are lovely little moths, and we must watch to see if we can spot any more.'

'I've got a lovely woolly-bear caterpillar at home, Uncle,' said John. 'I love those furry ones, don't you? What will my woolly-bear grow into, after he turns himself into a chrysalis?'

'Woolly-bear caterpillars become those beautiful garden tiger moths,' said Uncle Merry. 'You can't mistake them when you see them – big moths, with crimson bodies, crimson under-wings spotted with black, and white fore-wings also spotted with black. There are some lovely moths about at night now. Look out for the yellow under-wings, and the red and crimson under-wings – their names will tell you what they are like.'

'Uncle Merry, I saw a most ENORMOUS moth yesterday,' said John. 'It was almost as big as a sparrow and just as brown.'

'Storyteller!' said Janet, hoping that she would never in her life come across such a big moth.

'I'm not a storyteller!' said John indignantly. 'Am I, Uncle?'

'I shouldn't think so,' said Uncle Merry. 'The moth you saw must have been the kind we call old lady. It sometimes has a very wide wing-spread indeed, and is always dressed in sober brown.'

'There are as many insects about this month as there are flowers,' said Janet, watching a tiny coppery beetle rush along through the grass at her feet. 'What's this little gleaming coppery fellow, Uncle? I've seen so many.'

'Wood tiger beetle,' said Uncle Merry, after a glance. 'He's in a hurry, isn't he? Wood tigers always rush along like that, as if they were afraid of missing the train!'

'Let's sit down for a bit,' said Pat. 'We've walked a good way today, and I'm tired. Uncle, it's getting nice and cool now, isn't it? I like the summer evenings.'

They all sat down and rested themselves except Fergus, who went exploring by himself. Janet watched different kinds of beetles in the grass, and smacked flies and midges off her bare legs. She pointed to a cloud of slowly-flying insects.

'What are those flies?' she asked. 'They were high up just now, and then they came down lower.'

'Those are winged ants,' said Uncle Merry. 'Do you remember I told you that the female ants grew wings in the summer, and came up from their underground homes? The smaller winged ones you see are the males.'

A grasshopper jumped high in the air and landed beside Pat. It was gone before he could catch it. 'What powerful legs he must have to jump like that,' said Pat. 'Ah – now he is chirping. Can you hear him, Uncle?'

Uncle Merry nodded. His ears heard everything, and his eyes missed nothing. 'I can see a moth with the most lovely feelers,' he said. They all looked to where Uncle Merry pointed, and saw a big brown moth with white rings on his fore-wings, and beautiful feelers, just like a pair of feathers.

'That's the drinker moth,' said Uncle Merry.

'What does he drink?' asked John, with great interest.

'His caterpillar drinks the dewdrops,' said Uncle Merry. 'It's a quaint sight to see. So, because the caterpillar drinks dewdrops, the moth has the name of drinker.'

'You do tell us interesting things,' said Janet, picturing a caterpillar having a drink from a dewdrop. 'Oh, Uncle, what a lovely bright green moth!'

Fergus had gone into a bush and shaken the lower branches. From them fluttered a bright green moth. As soon as Uncle Merry said its name Janet felt that it was exactly the right one.

'The emerald moth,' said Uncle Merry. 'Pretty, isn't it?'

'Uncle, I'm going to learn every single moth and butterfly there is,' said John. 'I think they're so lovely.'

'Well, you'll be busy, John!' said Uncle Merry, with a laugh. 'There are hundreds and hundreds! I don't know half of them.'

Nobody believed this, for all the children thought that Uncle Merry knew everything.

A bat flew around their heads, and then another and another. Janet didn't even shrink back, and Uncle Merry glanced at her with pleasure.

'Moths to the left of her, moths to the right of her, bats in front of her, and bats behind her, and she doesn't squeal or jump,' he said. 'It's really marvellous, Janet!'

'I like bats now,' said Janet. 'I read all about them in one of our books, Uncle. They really do look like tiny flying mice, and did you know that they carry their babies with them when they fly? Uncle, have you ever heard a bat squeak? My book says they have such a high squeak that only people with very sharp ears can hear them.'

'Yes, I've heard them,' said Uncle Merry. 'Fergus, silly dog, you can never catch a bat! Look at him jumping up at them!'

It was time to go home. 'The evenings are getting shorter now,' said Janet. 'I wish they weren't. It's been a lovely summer, hasn't it, Uncle Merry? Soon it will be August, and oh dear, then it's September and we begin to go into the winter.'

'Cheer up, we're not there yet,' said Uncle Merry. 'Plenty of things to find and do before then.'

Home they went, tired and happy. John tried to remember all the names before he went to sleep, so that he could put them down on his different charts the next day. He fell asleep murmuring them.

'Drinker moth, harvest mouse, angelica, arrow-head, old lady. Oh dear, was old lady a moth or was it a flower?'

But John was asleep before he could remember.

The Great Big Fish

The Great Big Fish

MARY AND JOHN were on holiday at the seaside, and their mother said they could go to the jetty. It would be fun to run right to the end and see the deep green sea.

'Oh, John, I do wish we had a fishing rod like all the fishermen on the jetty,' said Mary. 'I would so like to catch a great big fish!'

'I believe these fishermen are going in for a fishing match,' said John. 'There are so many of them today!'

It was quite true. Five pounds was offered to the man who caught the biggest fish.

The children looked in the baskets of all the

fishermen as they passed. No one had caught a fish yet.

Suddenly they came to Mr Brown whom they knew last year.

'Have you caught a fish yet?' asked Mary.

'Not yet,' said Mr Brown. 'I think all the fish must know my line too well.'

The children had a grand time on the jetty. They watched the fishermen as they saw one after another pull up fine fish.

Mr Brown caught one too, but it was very tiny.

He waited and waited. The children had their lunch with them, so they sat by him and waited too.

'I'm stiff with sitting here so long,' he said at last. 'I'll go for a walk along the jetty and back. Do you mind staying by my rod while I go?'

'May I hold it for you?' asked John. 'I've never held a rod in my life. I'll be very careful.'

So Mr Brown let him hold the rod. Then off he went to stretch his legs.

Suddenly a most exciting thing happened! The rod

John was holding almost flew out of his hands!

'It's a fish!' yelled John. 'Mr Brown, where are you, where are you?'

But Mr Brown was at the end of the jetty. Mary caught hold of the rod too.

'Wind this little wheel on the rod like Mr Brown does!' she said to John.

So he wound in the line, and the fish on the end pulled and jerked – but John held it fast.

A fisherman came to help, but John said he was sure he could manage.

Mr Brown appeared again, and as soon as he saw what was happening he rushed to John. He took his rod and tried to land the fish – letting the line run out when the fish pulled hard, and reeling it in when he had a chance.

At last he had the fish. Another man had to catch it in a net as it flopped on to the pier, for it was so big.

'Mr Brown, your fish is the very biggest!' the children shouted. 'How much do you think it weighs?'

It was weighed on the scales, and it was eleven pounds! Mr Brown was so pleased. No one had caught such a big fish so far. Perhaps someone would catch a bigger one before the day was out. He would have to wait and see.

The children waited too. Every time a fisherman caught a fish they rushed to see how big it was – but no one caught such a big one as old Mr Brown.

At five o'clock, when the match ended, Mr Brown was given the prize of five pounds. He was so pleased that he couldn't stop smiling.

'You've had no tea,' he said to the children. 'You've been two big bits of luck for me, haven't you? Come along. We'll go and show this fine fish to everyone – then we'll have tea in a teashop. We'll have shrimp sandwiches, chocolate cream buns, and two ice creams each!'

So off they went, and how everyone stared in surprise at the big fish they carried!

Mother said of *course* they could go to tea with

Mr Brown. They ate a most enormous tea, and John and Mary thanked Mr Brown and said they had never had such a lovely day in their lives.

'Oh, it isn't finished yet!' said Mr Brown, beaming all over his red shining face. 'You must have a bit of my prize, you know, for you helped to catch the big fish! Now, what do you think you'd like, Mary? A doll? And you, John? A box of soldiers?'

'I'd like a little fishing rod please,' said John. 'And Mary would like one too. We would so like to go fishing ourselves!'

'Right!' said Mr Brown. So he bought them a fishing rod each, and then they went back to their mother, carrying their new rods very proudly.

Tomorrow they are going fishing on the jetty. Don't you wish you could be there too, to see the very first fish they catch?

Flip's Sunstroke

Flip's Sunstroke

'WHO'S THAT coming up to the door?' asked Binkle the bunny, peering out of the window.

'It looks like a beggar,' said Flip. 'No, it isn't. He's got something under his arm to sell.'

Rat-tat-tat! The door knocker made a terrific noise.

Binkle opened the door.

'Good morning,' said the visitor. 'May I come in and show you my pictures? I'm Firky Fox, and I paint pictures with my brush. Beauties they are, too, I can tell you.'

Binkle didn't like foxes.

'No, you can't come in,' he said. 'Show me your pictures here.'

Firky held them out one by one.

'Oak Tree Town at Sunset,' he said. 'A very nice one, that. See the red sunshine on the windows! And here's Bracken Hill with the snow on it. A real beauty!'

Flip came and peeped over Binkle's shoulder.

'We don't want pictures, Binkle,' he said.

'*Here's* a nice one now!' said Firky. 'A field of turnips.'

'Yes, that *is* nice,' agreed Binkle, wishing it was real. 'I'll take that one. Yes, and I'll have this one too, with the cabbages and lettuces on a dish. And that one with all those hazelnuts and acorns – and what about this one with the beetles and the cheese?'

'Oh Binkle!' gasped Flip in amazement. 'What in the world are you thinking of? You're not going to buy those pictures, surely?'

Binkle took no notice of Flip. He took out his purse, and counted out some money.

'There you are,' he said to Firky. 'I'll give you

that for these four pictures.'

'Thank you,' said Firky, handing them over. 'They're cheap at the price!'

He packed the rest of the pictures under his arm, and went off, whistling cheerfully.

Binkle carried the four pictures indoors, set them on the floor against the wall, and looked at them. Flip looked as if he thought Binkle was quite mad, and he rubbed his nose nervously with his paw.

'Do you feel quite well, Binkle?' he asked.

Binkle laughed.

'Yes,' he answered. 'And I haven't bought these pictures to hang up. Oh no, Flip! I've got a better idea than that.'

Flip groaned. 'What is it?' he asked. 'I shouldn't think we've got a single penny left after you've paid Firky Fox.'

'We haven't!' said Binkle cheerfully. 'But we're going to make LOTS of money with the help of these pictures.'

'How?' asked Flip curiously.

'Like this!' laughed Binkle, and picked up a piece of white chalk. He knelt on the floor and wrote with it. Then he sat down by the pictures, looking thoroughly miserable, and held out his cap.

ALL MY OWN WORK. PLEASE SPARE A
PENNY TO KEEP ME AND MY OLD FATHER

was what he had written on the floor.

'Oh!' gasped Flip. 'Binkle, you are dreadful! Whatever will you do next?'

'Any amount of things!' said Binkle, with a grin. 'First, I'm going to take these to Bracken Hill Town, where we're not well known. I'm going to find a nice sunny corner and sit down by my pictures. I shall have such a lovely lazy day, and only just have to count how many pennies come rolling in!'

'But what about your poor old father?' asked Flip. 'You haven't *got* a poor old father.'

'Oh yes I have!' chuckled Binkle. 'You're the poor

old father, Flip. I'm going to wrap you up in a shawl and muffler, and wheel you down to Bracken Hill Town in a bath-chair. You can go comfortably to sleep all day, if you like.'

Flip wriggled his nose and thought.

'All right,' he said at last. 'There doesn't seem to be much danger in your plan. I'll come.'

The two rascals began to make ready. Binkle fetched an old bath-chair out of the shed, and cleaned it up. Then he wrapped Flip in a big red shawl, tied a blue-spotted muffler round his head, and put him in the chair. He placed the pictures on Flip's knees and started off.

Over Bumble Bee Common he went, pushing Flip along quickly. Bumpity-bump! went the chair over the bracken and heather, and shook all the breath out of Flip's body!

'Let me get out and walk!' he begged. 'I can't stand this!'

'You're not standing it; you're sitting it,' answered

Binkle cheerfully, going faster than ever – so fast that poor Flip hadn't breath enough to say another word.

At last they arrived at Bracken Hill Town, and Binkle slowed down. He went down the village street, pushing Flip along, looking for a nice sunny corner.

'Here's one that will do,' he decided. 'It's sunny, and it's just near the marketplace, so there'll be lots of people passing.'

He wheeled Flip to the side, and fixed the chair so that it wouldn't run down the pavement. Then he spread out his pictures, wrote on the pavement with chalk, sat down on a cushion he had brought, and held out his cap.

Binnie Badger came hurrying by from market, carrying a bag full of potatoes. She stopped and looked at the pictures.

'That picture of the beetles is very good,' she said. 'You're a clever painter. Here's a penny for you,' and she put it into Binkle's cap.

'Thank you, ma'am,' said Binkle.

'Thank you, ma'am,' croaked Flip in a very quavery old voice.

Then came Susie Squirrel hurrying to market to buy nuts for dinner. When she saw the picture of nuts and acorns, she stopped with a squeak of delight.

'I almost thought they were real,' she said. 'They're just what I'm going to buy for dinner. Here's something for you,' and she threw a coin into Binkle's cap.

'Thank you kindly, ma'am,' said Binkle.

'What did she give you?' asked Flip in a whisper.

'Ha'penny,' answered Binkle. 'Sh! There's a lot of folk coming now!'

Bibs Bunny thought the turnip-field picture was wonderful and she gave Binkle a penny. So did Bobtail Bunny, her husband. Hickory Hare loved the picture of the cabbages and lettuces, and Mary Mouse thought the cheese picture was beautiful.

Soon Binkle's cap was jingling with pennies, and he could hardly stop himself whistling merrily.

'Fine supper we'll have tonight!' he whispered to Flip.

'I hope we *shall*,' said Flip. 'You've got the best of things, I can tell you. I'm getting hungry, and my! the sun is hot! Can't I take off this shawl, Binkle?'

'Good gracious, no!' said Binkle sharply. 'Everyone will see you're not an old rabbit, then. And don't stick your ears up straight like a youngster. Flop them down over your nose, as if you were tired out.'

Flip did so, and heaved a great sigh. Sally Stoat, who was just passing, felt very sorry for him.

'Poor old fellow!' she said. 'I'm sorry to see you're feeling ill. I'll give two pennies to your son, and perhaps he can buy you some medicine to make you better.'

She dropped two pennies into Binkle's cap and went on her way to market.

'Twopence! That will buy you a fine lot of medicine, Flip!' chuckled Binkle.

'You just try buying me medicine!' scowled Flip.

'Buy me some lemonade instead. I'm thirsty enough to drink a pailful.'

'That's a good idea of yours,' said Binkle. 'I'll leave you here for a minute and go and get you something to eat and drink.'

'Don't be long,' said Flip.

'No,' promised Binkle, and off he went down the street to look for a lemonade shop.

Flip began thinking of what Binkle might bring back. He thought happily for about ten minutes, then he began to wish Binkle would come back.

He craned his muffled neck round to the left, and looked down the street, but he could see no signs of Binkle!

'Oh, dear!' he groaned. 'I do think he might be quick. Ah! there's somebody! Perhaps it's Binkle!'

But it wasn't. It was Dinky Dormouse. She stopped opposite Flip's chair, and looked at him.

'So your son's gone and left you, has he?' she said. 'Well, I hope he'll soon come back. It isn't safe to leave an old fellow like you alone, in the road. Anything might happen.'

Flip began to feel alarmed.

'Whatever *has* happened to Binkle?' he thought anxiously. 'He said he wouldn't be long! And what can I do? I'm supposed to be an old rabbit, and can't walk. Folk would know we'd been playing a trick on them if I suddenly jumped out and went to look for Binkle. Oh, dear me!'

Still Binkle didn't come. Half an hour went by, and another half an hour!

Flip got more and more worried. He couldn't think what in the world to do. Folk stared at him in surprise, as they passed, and wondered why he was all alone. Flip couldn't bear it.

The sun got hotter and hotter, and he suddenly felt very sleepy. He struggled to keep his eyes open, but it was no good. They would keep shutting themselves – and in two minutes Flip was sound asleep, dreaming of lemonade and lettuces.

Presently Sally Stoat came back from market. She was very surprised to see that Flip was all alone.

'Where's your son gone?' she asked him.

Flip made no reply. He was dreaming hard.

'Where's your son gone?' asked Sally in a louder voice.

Flip went on sleeping.

Then Sally became alarmed, and bent over him. She saw his eyes were shut and she thought he must be ill.

'Poor old fellow!' she said. 'I think I'd better get help. Maybe he's got a sunstroke, sitting here in the sun!'

She beckoned to Dinky Dormouse, who was on her way back home.

'Dear, dear!' said Dinky in alarm. 'He was all alone when *I* passed, about half an hour ago. Hadn't we better do something?'

'Let's wheel him over to Hanna Hare's,' said Sally. 'Perhaps she'll know what to do for sunstroke.'

So together they unfixed the bath-chair and pushed

it up the street to Hanna Hare's.

'Whoever have you got there?' asked Hanna in surprise.

'A poor old rabbit with sunstroke,' explained Dinky. 'His son has left him, and we're afraid the poor old thing is ill. What do you do for sunstroke, Hanna?'

'We must put ice on his head and put him in a dark room,' said Hanna anxiously. 'Dear, dear, what a sad thing! But first we must unwrap him and get him out of his chair.'

All this time Flip had been soundly sleeping, and not even when he was being wheeled away did he awake. But when Dinky began pulling at the muffler round his neck, he woke up with a jump.

'Ow!' he said. 'Stop it, Binkle.'

Then he caught sight of Dinky and Sally and Hanna.

'Ooh!' he said. 'Am I dreaming?'

'No, no,' said Hanna soothingly. 'Not dreaming. We're just looking after you. You're not very well, and we want you to come and lie down.'

'Lie down indeed!' said Flip, pulling his shawl round him. 'I'm not going to get out of this chair, I tell you! Leave me alone.'

'Just let me unwind this hot muffler then,' begged Sally, trying to pull it off.

Flip knew what would happen if that came off, and showed him to be not an old rabbit, but a young bunny.

He made a growling noise and jerked his head back.

'I've got a *terrible* temper,' he shouted, 'so don't make me lose it! I'm a dreadful fellow when I'm roused, *though* I'm old. I *won't* have my muffler off!'

Dinky and Sally and Hanna looked at him in alarm.

'Yes, it's very bad sunstroke,' whispered Hanna. 'I'll get Hickory Hare, my husband, to come and hold him while I put some ice on his head. Stay here for a minute.'

She tiptoed out of the room and brought Hickory back with her. He held Flip firmly whilst Hanna tied a big lump of ice on his head. Flip was so hot that the ice melted and ran in little cold streams down his neck.

It was frightfully uncomfortable. But he didn't dare to struggle too much in case his shawl and muffler came off.

'Oh dear!' he thought. 'Why on earth did I let Binkle dress me up like this? I might have known trouble would come. Whatever *is* Binkle doing, anyway?'

Binkle at that very moment was hurrying back to where he had left Flip. He had gone to a greengrocer's and bought two fat turnips, which both he and Flip *loved* to eat raw; and then he had gone into a lemonade shop, sat down on a chair, and ordered two glasses of lemonade with parsley floating in it.

But when Rixie Rat brought it to him, he was fast asleep! He had put the two ha'pennies out on the table, so she took those, and didn't wake him.

And when he *did* wake up, my goodness! He *was* in a way!

'Whatever will poor old Flip be thinking!' he groaned. He drank one glass of lemonade, picked up the other, and ran off.

But when he got to his pictures, Flip wasn't there! Binkle rubbed his eyes, twitched his nose, and flapped his ears; but no, Flip still wasn't there!

'But where *can* he be gone to?' marvelled Binkle. 'The chair's gone too. It can't have gone away by itself. What a mystery! Oh, well! I may as well drink this lemonade before I look for him!'

He drank it off, and sat down to think.

'Flip can't be trusted by himself,' he said at last. 'I oughtn't to have left him. Perhaps he got tired and went home.'

This seemed to Binkle to be the only explanation for Flip's mysterious disappearance. So after a while he packed up his pictures and trotted off towards Bumble Bee Common.

When he got there he sniffed at the turnips inside the bag.

'Flip doesn't deserve any for scooting off like that,' he decided. 'And I'm hungry, so I'll just sit down here and eat them.'

He sat down and began munching, feeling quite sure Flip must be waiting for him at Heather Cottage.

But Flip wasn't. He was still in Hanna's drawing-room, getting in a worse and worse temper. He growled and fidgeted and flapped his ears and jiggled his chair until Hanna and Sally grew alarmed.

'I don't like it,' whispered Sally. 'Perhaps he's mad and hasn't got a sunstroke after all.'

'Perhaps so,' answered Hanna. 'What about fetching Wily Weasel over from Oak Tree Town? He'll find out where he belongs to, and take him back.'

Flip caught just two words of Hanna's whispering – and they were 'Wily Weasel', the name of his enemy, the policeman of Oak Tree Town.

It was too much for Flip. He gave a terrified yell, leapt from his chair, and jumped straight out of the open window into the street! Up the road he tore, his red shawl flapping behind him and his blue-and-white muffler streaming out like a flag!

'Oh! Oh!' shrieked Hanna and Sally and Dinky

in fright.

'Oh, look at him! Look at him!' gasped Sally in amazement. 'Would you believe that an old rabbit could jump and run like that?'

'He *must* be mad!' said Dinky nervously. 'It's a good thing he's gone!'

'What a surprising thing!' said Hanna Hare, fanning herself and panting a little from the shock. 'I wonder who he is and where he lives?'

Flip tore on up the street, scaring everybody he met. He was dreadfully angry – angry with Binkle for deserting him, frightened that Wily Weasel might catch him, and terribly uncomfortable in his shawl and muffler.

He stopped when he came to Bumble Bee Common and began to unwrap his muffler. Suddenly he heard a little humming sound nearby. He peeped round a tree to see who it was.

It was Binkle! Binkle, eating a large turnip and humming cheerfully!

Flip was so furious that for once he forgot to be a meek little bunny, and he gave a tremendous yell and pounced on Binkle.

Binkle dropped his turnips and gave a howl of terror at the sight of Flip with ice on his head. Then Flip was on top of him and in two minutes he was thoroughly shaken and smacked.

'That'll teach you to leave me tied up in a bath-chair!' said Flip fiercely. 'Now I'm going to take the turnips and have a good feast by myself at Heather Cottage. *And don't you dare to come near till I've finished!* Oh! and here's a present for you.'

Flip took some ice from his head and slipped it down Binkle's neck!

Then the indignant little rabbit stalked off – and Binkle was so surprised that he didn't even dare to follow him!

Nicky's Motor Car

Nicky's Motor Car

NICKY HAD a motor car. It was just big enough for himself, and he loved it very much. It was bright red, and had two lamps in front and a red one behind. But, what a pity, it hadn't a hooter!

Nicky was always wishing it had. He said so quite twenty times a day, and really, Mummy got quite tired of hearing it.

'Nicky, hooters cost about two pounds,' she said, 'and I haven't got two pounds to spare. Now run away, there's a good boy, and don't worry me any more.'

'Well, Mummy, I don't know what to *do*!' said Nicky. 'You see, I've got my car to drive about in, but there's nowhere to *go*. You won't let me go for a long drive into the country.'

'I should think not!' said Mummy. 'You may go as far as the shops and back and that's all. Now, go along, and don't let me hear another grumble about that hooter, *please*!'

Nicky opened the red door of his car, climbed in, sat down on the seat and shut the door. It had a little handle that shut the door properly, just like a real car. It was really lovely. But it *was* a pity it hadn't a hooter!

'Suppose I ran into somebody and there was an accident!' said Nicky to himself. 'If I can't hoot, how can I tell people to get out of the way? Really, I do *wish* I had a hooter. I wish Mummy would buy me one.'

He pedalled off down the path. He went out of the gate and very soon he met Harry, the boy over the road.

'Hallo,' said Harry. 'I do like your car.'

'Yes, but it hasn't got a hooter,' said Nicky. 'Isn't it a pity?'

'Well, why don't you get one?' asked Harry.

'Mummy hasn't the money to buy me one,' said Nicky.

'Well, good gracious, can't you get the hooter yourself?' said Harry. 'My mummy says that if you want a thing badly enough you can always find a way to get it!'

And he went off down the road, whistling. Nicky stared after him, thinking hard.

'Well!' he thought. 'That's an idea! Why should I expect other people to get me the things I want? Why shouldn't I try to get them myself? I could perhaps earn some money to buy the hooter!'

So he pedalled off to Mrs Jones, who had once given him twenty pence for running an errand. She was at the garden gate, looking for Dick, her big boy.

'Hallo, Nicky,' she said. 'Have you seen Dick? I want him to go down to the chemist for me.'

'No, I haven't seen him,' said Nicky. 'But I'll go for you, Mrs Jones.'

He didn't say anything about his hooter, or how he hoped Mrs Jones might give him twenty pence. Mummy had always told him he must do things for nothing, and then, if people *were* kind enough to give something to him, that was a nice surprise!

'Oh, thank you,' said Mrs Jones. 'It won't take you long in that nice car of yours. Run along and ask them to give you a packet of cotton wool for Mrs Jones.'

So off went Nicky pedalling away fast. He came to the chemist shop and parked his car outside. He went in and asked for the cotton wool. He took the big packet out and put it on the seat beside the wheel. There was just room for it. Back he pedalled to Mrs Jones.

'Good boy!' she said. 'You've been quick! Here is twenty pence!'

'Oh, thank you, Mrs Jones,' said Nicky, pleased, and he put it into his pocket. The first twenty pence!

Then he pedalled away again, wondering how he could earn more.

He met old Mrs Lacy, and she had so many parcels that she really didn't know how to carry them all. Nicky pedalled up to her.

'Mrs Lacy! Put your parcels into my car and I'll carry them for you,' he said. Mrs Lacy looked down, very pleased indeed.

'Kind child!' she said, and she put her parcels into the little motor car. Nicky pedalled proudly in front of her with them, all the way home. Then he handed her out the parcels.

'I wonder if you'd like an orange in return for your kindness, or twenty pence to spend?' said Mrs Lacy, smiling at him.

'Well, I don't mind having nothing at all, if you can't afford it,' said Nicky, remembering that Mrs Lacy was poor. 'But if you can, I'd love to have twenty pence. You see, I'm saving up for a new hooter.'

'Ah! Then you certainly must have the money,' said

Mrs Lacy, and she handed twenty pence to him. Nicky said thank you and put it into his pocket. Nicky had forty pence already!

'If you pedal down to my sister, Mrs White, maybe she will have a job for you too,' said Mrs Lacy. 'I know she is very busy this morning.'

So Nicky pedalled off to the little old cottage where Mrs White lived. She was taking the eggs out of her hen-house and counting them.

'Good morning, Mrs White,' said Nicky politely, raising his cap. 'Mrs Lacy told me to come and see if there was anything I could do for you.'

'You're just the person I want!' said Mrs White. 'Can you take a basket of eggs to Miss Brown, do you think – and then come back again and take two dozen to Mr Thomas over the hill? My leg is bad this morning and I really can't walk all that way.'

'Oh yes, certainly,' said Nicky, and he took the basket at once. He pedalled away to Miss Brown's – and do you know, wasn't it surprising, she gave him twenty pence for bringing the eggs! That really was a surprise to Nicky!

'Now I've got sixty pence!' he said, and he went back to Mrs White's for the other eggs. He took them to Mr Thomas, but he didn't get any money there, for Mr Thomas was not a very kind old man.

He took a third lot of eggs to the dairy as well, and when he went back to tell Mrs White he had done that and was there anything else, she said no – and gave him forty pence!

'You're a kind little chap,' she said. 'You deserve a reward.'

'But Miss Brown gave me twenty pence when I left her eggs,' said Nicky. 'You should only give me ten pence, Mrs White, because I've already got twenty for the eggs.'

But Mrs White made him have forty – so now he had one pound! He was getting rich. He pedalled to the toyshop to see how much a hooter was, and he found that he could get a beautiful one for one pound and eighty pence; a really good one that would hoot like a proper car – not a silly little pip-pip one like Sophie had on her bicycle.

On the way home Nicky had a real piece of luck. Whatever do you suppose it was? He *found* ten pence lying on the path! Think of that! Nobody was about so he couldn't ask anyone if they had dropped it. He got out of his car and picked up the coin. Now he had one pound ten pence!

'It's time for dinner,' said Nicky. 'I'm hungry. Perhaps this afternoon I can earn some more money. Oh, this is better than asking other people to buy me things! I feel much prouder when I'm doing it all myself.'

Now, when he was sitting down to dinner, Mother suddenly said, 'Oh, it's your cousin Robert's birthday tomorrow, Nicky. You should buy him a present. Have you anything in your money box?'

'No, Mummy,' said Nicky. 'I took out all my money to buy Daddy a new pipe for *his* birthday.'

Nicky went rather red when he said this, for he knew quite well he had over a pound in his pocket. He didn't say a word about it. Oh, he really couldn't spend on Robert, when he had worked so hard to get to buy a new hooter.

'Poor Robert is ill,' said Mummy, giving Nicky some pudding. 'It will be so nice for him to have a few presents tomorrow. He can't even have a piece of his birthday cake, poor boy, and no party at all.'

Nicky listened, and felt his money. He was sorry for Robert. It was dreadful, really dreadful, not to be able to eat birthday cake on a birthday. Suddenly he made up his mind. He would spend his money on Robert!

'Mummy, I earned over a pound this morning by going on errands,' he said. 'I meant to save it up to buy a hooter, but I'll buy Robert something instead.'

'That's very generous of you, Nicky,' said Mummy. 'I'm proud of you.'

Nicky was pleased to hear his mother say that.

He did like her to be proud of him. He went out in the afternoon and spent a long time in the toyshop, choosing something for Robert. At last he bought a top, a book and a toy motor car. He thought Robert would rather have three things than one if he were ill.

But he didn't look at the hooters at all. He really couldn't.

The next day he went round in his motor car with the three small parcels. His Auntie Ellen was pleased to see him. She said he might come in and see Robert for just two minutes.

So in he went and gave him the three presents. Robert was simply delighted. He was in bed, and his bed was scattered with all kinds of presents.

'It's very kind of you, Nicky,' he said, undoing the parcels. 'The top is lovely – and the book I'll read today – and the motor car will just fit my new garage.'

Nicky was pleased. Then Robert said something surprising.

'I say, Nicky,' he said. 'Look! Someone has sent me

a hooter – but I haven't got a car or tricycle, so would you like it for *your* car? I know you've got that lovely red one and it hasn't got a hooter, has it?'

'Oh, Robert! Don't you really want it?' cried Nicky, getting red with excitement, for the hooter was a much nicer one than he had meant to buy. 'Oh, Robert, it's *exactly* what I wanted! Can you really spare it?'

'Of course I can,' said Robert. 'Mummy doesn't like the noise it makes, and I haven't got a car – so what's the use of it? Take it, and use it for your car!'

So Nicky took it, and he fitted it to his car. And now, my goodness, you always know when he is coming! Hoot-a-toot-too! Hoot-a-toot-too! goes that big hooter, and people think there's a *real* car coming and don't they jump out of the way!

Nicky deserved it, don't you think so?

The Very
Forgetful Gnome

The Very
Forgetful Gnome

ONE DAY Twiddle the enchanter heard of a marvellous broom. His friend, Mother Doodah, told him of it.

'It's really wonderful!' she said. 'This broom, if stood just outside your door, Twiddle, knows at once if an enemy is coming to see you. When the enemy is just about to knock at the door the broom rushes out from its corner and sweeps him right down the garden path into the nearest puddle.'

'What a marvellous thing!' said Twiddle, who had a great many enemies and was often bothered by them.

'I really think I must get that broom. It would be most useful to me. Who has it now, Mother Doodah?'

'The gnome, Mister Dithery, has it, I think,' said Mother Doodah. 'He has had it for about fifty years, so people say. If it isn't worn out by now you could probably buy it from him.'

'I'll certainly try!' cried Twiddle, and he put on his best cloak and tallest hat at once. With him he carried a leather bag in which he had put twenty gold pieces. He thought he would have to pay highly for such a marvellous broom.

Dithery the gnome lived in a crooked house at the end of Humpty Village. Twiddle soon found it when he asked his way, and he strode up the path to the yellow front door, jingling all his money in his bag.

Blim-blam! He knocked loudly.

'Put the potatoes down on the step!' cried a husky voice from inside. 'I'm busy.'

'I haven't brought any potatoes!' the enchanter shouted indignantly. 'Open the door.'

'I tell you, I'm busy!' said the voice, crossly. 'If you are the washing, just leave it till next week.'

'I'm not the washing either!' shouted Twiddle, stamping his foot. 'I'm Twiddle the enchanter and I've come to buy something from you.'

'Oh! Well, why didn't you say so before?' said the husky voice. There came the *thud-thud* of big feet and the door was opened. Twiddle stepped inside. Dithery was a strange-looking gnome. His head was enormous, and he had a curious beard, which was neatly parted in two and tied up with blue ribbons.

'Good morning,' said Twiddle, looking all round. 'I've come to buy your broom. You know – the magic one that sweeps up enemies.'

'Oh, that one!' said Dithery, rubbing his long nose. 'Well, now, I haven't seen it for a very long time. I wonder what I did with it.'

'Don't you use it?' asked Twiddle in great surprise.

'Oh no, not now,' said the gnome. 'Not for a good many years. You see, people got so afraid of being swept up that everybody decided to be friends with me. So the broom was no longer any use for sweeping up my enemies, and I used it for an ordinary broom. It was fine for sweeping up the yard.'

'Fancy using a magic broom for yard rubbish,' said the enchanter, in horror. 'You don't deserve to have anything valuable, Dithery, really you don't! Tell me where the broom is.'

'What are you going to give me for it?' asked Dithery, twisting his beard round his fingers and messing up his nice blue ribbons.

'Well, I've brought a very large price for it,' said Twiddle, jingling his leather bag. 'Twenty whole golden pieces.'

'Ooh!' said Dithery, his eyes opening wide. 'That's fine. Give them to me, please. I want to buy a horse for myself. There's a lovely one for sale in our village.'

Twiddle counted out the money into Dithery's horny hand. The gnome went to the door and whistled. A small pixie came running up. The gnome gave him the twenty gold pieces and told him to go at once and buy the blue-spotted horse that Mister Ho-Ho had for sale.

'And bring it back to me this morning,' he ordered. The pixie ran off down the road.

'Now, Dithery, just tell me where the magic broom is, quickly!' said Twiddle impatiently. He had been looking all round, but he couldn't see it anywhere.

'Let me see now,' said Dithery, thinking so hard that his head swelled up like a balloon. 'You might look under the sink there. That's a likely place for it.'

Twiddle looked under the sink. To his surprise there were four little folding tables neatly stacked there, one against another.

'There's no broom here, Dithery,' he said. 'There are only a lot of little folding tables.'

'Dear me, so that's where I put those tables,' said Dithery. 'I wondered where they were. I got them for a party I was going to have, and then lost the tables. So I couldn't have the party.'

Twiddle looked at him in astonishment. Fancy forgetting things like that!

'Well, where else do you think the broom might be?' he asked.

'Let me think,' said Dithery. 'Oh yes – it might be in that cupboard over there. I'm sure I put it there, Twiddle.'

Twiddle opened the cupboard door, and out fell a great collection of cardboard boxes of all sizes. *Crash, crash!* They fell on his head and made him jump terribly.

Dithery began to laugh. 'Oh, dear,' he said. 'I'm really very sorry about that, Twiddle. I quite forgot I had emptied that cupboard to make room for my boxes. I always save every box I get, you know, just in case I want one for anything. I needed one yesterday and couldn't find them anywhere – so I'm pleased to know where they are.'

'Whatever's the good of saving them if you forget where you've put them?' said Twiddle in disgust, kicking them back into the cupboard and slamming the door. 'Well, where did you put the things you turned out of this cupboard, Dithery? Do try and think.'

'All right,' said Dithery, screwing up his face. 'Yes – I put them all in the oven. There didn't seem to be room anywhere else.'

'In the oven?' said Twiddle, staring in amazement at the gnome. 'Are you mad, Dithery? Whatever made you put them in the *oven*?'

Twiddle went to the stove and pulled open the oven door. Inside lay a mass of half-burnt things – blackened brushes, a broken dustpan, a lot of useless tins of polish.

'Goodness!' said Dithery, looking at them as the enchanter raked them all out. 'So that's what that terrible smell was last month. I couldn't think what it could be! I suppose all those things got cooked when I lit the fire.'

Twiddle thought of quite a lot of things to say but

they were all too rude, so he didn't say anything at all, but just thought that Dithery was the stupidest gnome he had ever come across. He poked about among the half-burnt things, but to his delight there was no broom there. He had been very much afraid that he would find it burnt so that it would be of no use at all – but it wasn't there.

'Dithery, think again,' he said at last. 'The broom isn't in the oven.'

'Oh yes, I remember now,' said Dithery, cheering up. 'I put it in . . . oh! Look! There's my new horse!'

There was a sound of clip-clopping hoofs and a horse looked in at the door. Twiddle thought it was a most peculiar creature, not at all worth twenty golden pieces. It was covered with bright blue spots, and wore spectacles and a hat tied up with a yellow ribbon.

'Brrrooomph!' said the odd-looking horse, politely.

'Oh, you darling!' cried Dithery, dancing up to it. 'I'll go for a ride on you straight away!'

He was just going to climb up on the horse's back when Twiddle caught hold of his legs and pulled him firmly away. 'No,' he said. 'No, Dithery! You will not go for a ride. You will not do anything until you have found me that magic broom. Go out, horse!'

'Brrrooomph!' said the horse, in disappointment, and out it went. It sat down on a seat in the garden. Twiddle thought it was the strangest horse he had ever seen.

'Now, Dithery, think again and tell me where that broom is,' he said.

Dithery's head swelled up once more, which showed Twiddle that he was really thinking.

'I might have put it in the dog-kennel,' he said at last, in his husky voice.

'The dog-kennel!' said Twiddle, in astonishment. 'Whatever for?'

'Well, I must have somewhere to put things, mustn't I?' said Dithery, rather sulkily. 'I often put things into the dog-kennel. There's no dog there, and the kennel would be wasted if I didn't use it for something!'

Twiddle went into the yard where a big dog-kennel stood in one corner. He looked inside. To his enormous surprise it was full of potatoes!

'Dithery! This dog-kennel is full of potatoes!' cried Twiddle.

'Oh my, of course! I did put the potatoes there,' said Dithery, running out. 'I quite forgot. No wonder I couldn't find them when I looked in the vegetable rack. Now I shall be able to have potatoes for my dinner again.'

'Dithery, will you please think where the broom is,' begged Twiddle, who was beginning to feel he was in a most annoying sort of dream. 'Do remember!'

'Well, I keep remembering!' replied Dithery, most indignantly. 'I've remembered all sorts of places.'

'But not the right ones,' said Twiddle, patiently. 'Just remember the right one, now.'

'Well – you might look in the kitchen cupboard on

the top shelf,' said Dithery. 'I often put things there out of the way.'

Twiddle thought it was a funny sort of place to put a broom, but he went to the cupboard door and opened it. He looked on the top shelf, but all he could see on it was a large round tin. He opened it – and found a bright yellow coat!

'Dithery! There's no broom here – only a round tin and inside it is a yellow coat! Whatever made you put a yellow coat here?'

'Ooh!' squeaked Dithery in delight. 'So that's where I put my yellow coat. I wondered where it could be! It's my best one. Pass it to me, Twiddle. I've had to wear my old one for a long time now. Oh, I remember – I put it there because my wardrobe was so full of other things.'

Twiddle snorted angrily and threw the coat to Dithery. He was delighted to have his best coat back.

'What was your wardrobe so full of that you couldn't even put your coat there?' Twiddle asked.

'I suppose you keep your coal there, or something like that?'

'Well, yes, I believe my coal is there,' said Dithery. He walked into his bedroom and opened the door of the wardrobe – but it wasn't full of coal after all. It was simply crammed with fishing nets!

'Must you keep fishing nets in your wardrobe?' asked Twiddle, in a tired sort of voice. 'People don't usually, you know. Whatever made you get so many nets, anyway?'

'Oh, somebody said there was a big fish in the village pond,' said Dithery. 'So I bought those nets to catch it. But I forgot where I'd put them. I should have caught that fish easily if only I'd had my nets, I know I should.'

'Where did you put the things you took out of the wardrobe when you put the nets in?' asked Twiddle, feeling that he really would like to pinch Dithery, or slap him, or do something really horrid to him. He was the most annoying person that Twiddle had ever met.

'Let me see,' said Dithery. 'I kept my garden tools there, I think – so the broom might have been among them. Now where did I put them?'

A piece of coal fell out of the fire while he was thinking and Dithery bent to sweep up the mess. He took up a flat broom-head that stood on the hearth – and then he gave a loud yell that made Twiddle jump nearly out of his skin.

'Here's the broom!' he cried. 'Of course! I quite forgot I'd been using it for the fire. I took off the handle and just used the broom-head. It is very good for sweeping up ashes.'

Twiddle stared at the old, dirty, blackened broom-head in horror.

'Do you mean to say that you took off the handle and used a valuable magic broom to sweep up ashes?' he said sternly.

'Well, it wasn't much use for anything else,' said the gnome, sulkily. 'I haven't any enemies at all now.'

'You'll make an enemy of me if you go on like this,'

said Twiddle, fiercely. 'I've wasted all my morning looking in stupid places for that broom, and finding all kinds of silly things for you, and the broom was there under my nose all the time. Now where's the handle?'

'I really can't imagine,' said Dithery, cheerfully.

Twiddle went almost mad with rage. He bent down and shouted in Dithery's ear.

'Tell me where that handle is or I'll turn you into a box of matches and strike you till you're all used up!' he yelled. 'This broom is no use without its handle.'

'Don't get cross with me or I shan't be able to remember anything at all,' said Dithery, sulking.

'Well, you haven't remembered anything of any use so far,' said Twiddle, gloomily.

'I think I know where the handle is,' said Dithery, suddenly. 'Yes, I do! I made a bird table, and used the handle for a pole to put the tray-piece of the table on, to put it out of reach of cats, you know.'

'What! You used the handle of a magic broom to

make a bird-table!' cried Twiddle, horrified. 'Well, you don't deserve to have anything valuable at all. You really don't.'

He looked out into the garden for the bird table, but he couldn't see one anywhere.

'I suppose you've tied the bird-table to the chimney or done something just as silly,' he grumbled. 'Where is it, Dithery?'

'It's under my bed,' said Dithery. 'I put it there, I know, but I can't remember why, now.'

'Probably because you wanted to make things really difficult for the birds!' said Twiddle, shaking his head in wonder at Dithery's brains. 'All right – I'll get it.'

He went into the bedroom and looked under the bed – and wonder of wonders, the bird-table really was there! Its broom-handle leg stuck out, and it wasn't many seconds before Twiddle had it in his hand. Now he had both the broom-head and the broom-handle. Good! At last he could go home.

He fitted the head to the handle and made a proper broom. Dithery watched him.

'There you are!' he said. 'Now you've got the old broom, you see – and I'm going to go for a ride on my nice new horse. Goodbye!'

He ran out into the garden, and the horse stood up. 'Brrrooomph!' he went. 'Brrrooomph!'

Dithery jumped up on to his back, and off they galloped down the path, the horse's spectacles jerking up and down on his big nose.

Twiddle put the broom over his shoulder and walked down the path and out of the gate, delighted to have the magic broom at last. He walked down the street and as he passed a little twisted cottage, with twelve tall chimneys rising from its roof, someone called him.

'Hi! Road sweeper! Will you come and sweep my path for me? It's very untidy with all the fallen leaves.'

'I'm not a road sweeper,' said Twiddle, indignantly.

'Well, that's a road-sweeping broom, isn't it?'

asked the little person in surprise, leaning out of her window to look.

'Indeed it's not!' said Twiddle. 'It's a very magic broom indeed. It once belonged to Dithery the gnome, and he has sold it to me this morning for twenty golden pieces.'

The little pixie-like person stared at Twiddle in surprise, and then she began to laugh very loudly indeed.

'Ho-ho, he-he!' she giggled. 'You don't mean to say that you've paid Dithery twenty golden pieces for that old broom over your shoulder? Why, that's not the magic broom! He sold that to my aunt five years ago, but I expect he's forgotten all about it by now. He's a marvellous forgetter, you know! Oh, what a joke! Where is Dithery now? You'd better go and get back your money.'

'He bought a blue-spotted horse and has gone riding on it,' said Twiddle, in a great rage. He flung the broom down on the ground and snorted so angrily that the little pixie woman looked quite alarmed.

'Oh, so he's bought that horse, has he?' she said. 'Well, it's no good waiting for him to come back, then. He's gone to visit his Aunt Dumpling, a thing he's been waiting to do for years and years. Only a blue-spotted horse knows the way, and he's been longing to buy one. He won't be back for at least a year.'

'Where does your aunt live?' asked Twiddle, gloomily. 'I suppose I'll have to go and buy the magic broom from her. All I hope is that she's got a better memory than Dithery the gnome has.'

'Oh yes,' said the little pixie person. 'She keeps the magic broom on her front doorstep and it sweeps up all her enemies nicely. You'd better take that frown off your face before you call on her or else the broom will think you're an enemy and will sweep you up!'

Off went poor Twiddle to buy the broom. He really did buy it, this time, and took it home with him. It swept up all his enemies beautifully. He has just heard that Dithery the gnome has come back from his visit to his aunt – and has sent him a note asking him to come and see him.

'He's my enemy!' he has told the broom, fiercely. 'So mind you sweep him up very roughly indeed, and land him *splash!* in the biggest puddle there is!'

But I don't expect old Dithery will remember to go and call on Twiddle, do you?

Somebody Saw!

IT WAS Sports Day at the big boys' school. All the Johns, Bills, Peters and Mikes were hoping to win a prize of some kind. How they practised their running and jumping and how they tried out the three-legged race for days beforehand! There were to be bicycle races too – quick ones and slow ones and trick ones.

Most of the boys had bicycles, and they cleaned them up before the great day. George cleaned his up, too.

George's bicycle was very old. It wanted a coat of paint. Its pedals had very worn rubbers, and it was bent in several places.

'But it's a good old bike, all the same,' George often said, when the other boys laughed at it. 'I'm fond of it. It's taken me for miles and miles, and I've had jolly good times on it.'

It *was* a good old bike, and George had never had a single accident on it. For one thing his father made him read the Highway Code till he almost knew it by heart – and for another thing he made George learn his manners.

Not only manners at home and at school – but manners on the road! 'You just remember that there are other people on the road, George,' he said. 'And don't forget that a spot of good manners can prevent an accident as often as keeping the Rules of the Road!'

So George waved on other bicyclists who wanted to pass him, instead of trying to out-race them, or swerving out at them as they passed. He stopped at the pedestrian crossings to let people walk over the road, instead of ringing his bell violently and making them jump. He put his hand out in good time before he turned a corner.

He was an excellent cyclist, and he had made up his mind to win one of the cycling prizes at the sports. If only he had a better bicycle!

'Harry's got one of the new racers,' he thought as he cleaned his. 'And John's just got a fine new one, as fast as any I've seen. And Patrick's bike is a beauty.'

He cycled off to school, in good time for the Sports. The parents had been asked to come too. They all turned up, hoping that their boys would win prizes. It was a hot, sunny day, just right for School Sports.

George was no good at running. He wasn't much good at jumping either, and Patrick easily won the high jump. Harry won the long jump. Then came the three-legged race. George was tied to Jeffrey, who got a fit of giggles, and down they both went at once!

'Aren't you ever going to win something, George?' asked his mother, when he went over to her. 'We've already had eight events, and you've been almost last in every one!'

'Wait till the cycling match,' said George. 'I'll win something there!'

But he didn't. He was a long way last in the speed race. How could anyone hope to go as fast as Harry on his new racer, or Patrick on his red and gold bike?

He didn't even win the slow bicycle race, because someone bumped into him and made him fall off. He was fourth in the trick-cycling, which was riding without touching the handlebars at all.

'I would have been first if my bike hadn't been so old,' he told his mother. 'You see, it's not properly balanced now. I haven't won a thing! I'm sorry, Mother, because though I don't mind, I know you're disappointed!'

'I am rather,' said his mother. 'Your father was so good at sports when he was a boy.'

The Sports came to an end. The prizes were given out and George looked admiringly at Harry's new cricket-bat and the grand football that John went up to get. The prizes were really very good indeed.

Then the boys went home. 'Now be careful, because you're all going off together,' said the Head.

'Don't act the goat – and remember, there are others on the road besides yourself!'

A lot of the boys did play the fool, of course. They always did. George couldn't help laughing when he saw Peter riding solemnly backwards down the road, instead of forwards, just as he had done in the trick cycling.

The boys didn't see a car following them slowly. They tore across the pedestrian crossing and made a woman with a pram scream, because she was already halfway across.

George stopped. 'I say – don't be scared! Look, you've dropped your book.' The woman was frightened and angry.

'You bad boys! Where are your manners, I'd like to know! I'll complain about you to your headmaster!'

George rode on. Behind came the car, very slowly. It stopped when George had got off his bicycle. George caught up with the others, who were waiting for a traffic light to change. Two cars were there, too. The boys swerved their bicycles in front of the cars as soon as the lights changed, preventing them from getting off quickly. One of the motorists hooted.

George waited, knowing that the cars would soon be well ahead of him. Then on he went again, and behind him came the car. He heard it and looked round. He swerved in to the kerb and waved it on courteously, and then waved on a man on a bicycle who seemed in a hurry.

The car stopped a little way in front. George saw two policemen in it. The driver beckoned to him. Oh dear – had he done anything wrong?

'Name and address?' he said to poor George. 'And school, please?'

George gave them, his heart sinking. 'What have I done, sir?' he said.

'Done?' said the police-driver, with a broad smile. 'Well, you've just won the Courtesy Prize for this town, that's all! We've been cruising round all day looking for someone on the roads who knows his Highway *Manners* as well as his Highway Rules – and you're the first person we've seen who knows them both.'

'I *say*!' said George, astonished and delighted. 'I've won a prize today, after all! I messed up everything I did at the Sports – and won a prize going home! What a bit of luck!'

The prize was a silver wristwatch with his name on it – and it was presented by the police on the platform of George's school. The Head was delighted and how the boys clapped George!

'Good old George! He's won something for the school! We've got the Courtesy Prize because of George.'

George still has the watch and it's a beauty. I know, because I've seen it!

The Little
Paper-Folk

The Little
Paper-Folk

ONE VERY wet afternoon, Jimmy and Susan thought they would cut out pictures from a magazine. Mother said they might, so they found their scissors, took two old magazines from the newspaper box in the garage, and went to the living room to cut out.

'I'm going to cut out these motor cars,' said Jimmy. 'They're good ones, all in colour. Look, Susan.'

'Yes,' said Susan. 'Well, I shall cut out some people. See, there's an old woman carrying a basket, and a tall man in a top hat, and a little man in a dressing gown. I shall cut out lots of people.'

Jimmy soon cut out his cars. There were three – one

red, one green and one blue. Then he thought he would cut out smaller things. There was a fish-slice, a kitchen spoon, a ladle, and a whisk on one page, so he cut those out. Then he found a page of boxes of chocolates, all with their lids open to show the chocolates inside. They did look delicious.

'I shall cut out these boxes of chocolates,' he said to Susan. 'Oh, what a nice lot of little people you have cut out! Stand them up against something, Susan. They will look real then.'

Susan stood them up. There was the old woman, the tall man, the little man in a dressing gown, a green imp, and a fat boy bouncing a ball. She stood them all up against a book.

'We've cut out lots of things,' she said. 'Cars and people, kitchen tools and boxes of chocolates. Oh, Jimmy, wouldn't it be lovely if those chocolates were real?'

'Let's take everything we've cut out to the big windowsill,' said Jimmy, gathering up his paper cars and other things. 'We'll stand the cars up and the people too. They will look splendid.'

So they went to the windowsill, behind the big blue curtain, and began to stand up all their paper things.

'I wish, I wish we were as small as these little people,' said Susan. 'Then we could play with them and see what they are really like.'

Well, I don't quite know how it happened, but there must have been some magic about that day, for no sooner had Susan wished her wish than it came true!

Yes, it really did! She and Jimmy grew smaller and smaller and they felt very much out of breath, for it all happened so quickly. But when at last they stopped growing small, they found themselves on the windowsill with the paper people and cars. And the paper people were alive!

They smiled at Susan and Jimmy, and came to shake hands with them. Their hands were funny – all flat and papery – and when the old woman turned round, Jimmy saw that she hadn't a proper back – there were printed letters all over her!

'That's the other side of the page she was cut out of!' whispered Jimmy, as he saw Susan's look of surprise. 'There was a story on the other side, and that's part of it. Isn't it strange?'

'We are glad you cut out such lovely boxes of chocolates for us,' said the man in the top hat, picking up a box and looking at it.

'And I'm glad you cut out my ball for me,' said the little fat boy. He began to bounce the ball but, alas, it would not bounce properly, because Susan's scissors had cut into the ball in one little place.

The boy was cross. 'The ball won't bounce properly,' he said frowning. 'You were careless when you cut it out! I don't like you after all!'

'Don't take any notice of him,' said the little man in the dressing gown. 'He's a bad-natured boy. I am pleased with the way you cut out my dressing gown. Look, even my belt is well cut out, so that I can tie it round me.'

The man in the top hat picked up a box of chocolates and offered them to Susan.

But she couldn't get her fingers into the box! You see, it was only a painted box, so of course the chocolates couldn't be taken out. She was so disappointed.

'I can't take out any of the chocolates,' she said, trying hard.

The green imp she had cut out came and looked at the box. He put up his little green hand and, to Susan's surprise, he picked out a handful of the chocolates and ran off with them.

'I expect he can do it because he's made of paper like the chocolates,' whispered Jimmy. 'Anyway, they'd taste horrid, I'm sure!'

'Let's go for a ride in these cars,' cried the old woman with the basket. They ran to the cars. The tall man took the wheel of the red car and the old lady climbed in beside him. That left the imp all alone with the green car, and he looked as black as thunder.

'I can't drive a car,' he said. 'One of you children must get in with me and drive me along. I'm not going to be left out!'

'I don't want to get in the car with you,' said Jimmy. 'I don't like the look of you.'

'You nasty boy!' cried the imp, in a rage. 'Get into the car at once. How dare you insult one of the paper-folk!'

To Jimmy's surprise all the other paper-folk sided with the green imp. They shouted angrily to the children:

'Get in and drive him! Get in and drive him! You wouldn't eat our chocolates, and now you're too grand to drive our car!'

The children felt quite scared. Jimmy went to the green car and tried to get in. But of course he couldn't because it was only paper. He tried and tried, but his leg simply slid down the paper to the ground.

The imp was sitting in the back, watching. He

frowned at Jimmy, and cried out crossly, 'You're only pretending not to be able to get in. You're only pretending! Why can't you get in? You're the same as us, aren't you, and we got in?'

'Well, we're not the same as you, so there!' said Jimmy, losing his temper. 'You're only made of paper – you haven't even got proper backs! We're real. You're just cut-out people; and your cars are cut-out cars, so of course we can't get into them! Don't be so silly!'

Well, when the paper-folk heard Jimmy saying that, they were all as hurt and angry as could be. They climbed out of the cars and looked all round them for something to fight the children with. They suddenly saw the fish-slice, the ladle, the kitchen spoon and the whisk that Jimmy had cut out, lying on the ground by the boxes of chocolates.

The tall man picked up the fish-slice, and the man in the dressing gown picked up the kitchen spoon. The imp snatched up the ladle. The old woman used her basket and the boy took the whisk to fight with, and together all the paper-folk rushed angrily at the scared children.

'Don't be frightened, Susan,' said Jimmy. 'They're only paper.'

'But we haven't anything to fight them with,' cried Susan, looking round on the windowsill.

'Let's blow them with our breath,' shouted Jimmy. 'They are only paper, you know.'

So, much to the cut-out people's surprise, as soon as they were close to the children, Jimmy and Susan blew hard at them with all their breath.

'Wheeew!' went the children together, and the paper-folk were all blown over flat! What a surprise for them! They picked themselves up and rushed at the children once more.

'Wheeeew!' blew Jimmy and Susan, and once again the paper-folk were blown down flat – and, oh my, the fat boy was blown right over the edge of the windowsill on to the floor below. How the paper-folk screamed to see him go!

'I shan't have much breath left soon,' whispered Jimmy to Susan. 'Whatever shall we do?'

'I wish we could grow to our own size again,' wailed Susan, who had had quite enough of being small.

Well, she only had to wish for it to become true, for there was still a little magic floating about in the air. Just as the paper-folk were rushing at them again the children shot up tall, and the cut-out people cried out in surprise.

In an instant the children were their own size, and at that moment they heard their mother's voice.

'Wherever are you? Jimmy! Susan! I've been looking for you everywhere!'

'Here we are, Mum,' said Jimmy, peeping round the window-curtain.

'But you weren't there a minute ago, Jimmy, for I looked to see,' said Mother in astonishment. 'There were only a few bits of paper blowing about on the windowsill. Now, where have you been hiding?'

'Truly we were there, Mum,' said Jimmy, and he and Susan told her of their adventure with the paper-folk.

But their mother laughed and wouldn't believe it. 'Don't make up such silly tales,' she said. 'Fighting with paper-folk indeed! Whoever heard such nonsense?'

'Well, Mummy, look!' cried Susan suddenly. 'Here's that nasty little boy on the floor, with his ball. Jimmy blew him over the edge of the windowsill. That just proves we are telling the truth.'

It did, didn't it? The children and their mother looked at the paper boy on the floor, and at the other paper-folk who were all lying quietly on the windowsill.

'I should stick them firmly into your scrapbook,' said Mother. 'Then they won't do any more mischief!'

So that's where the paper-folk are now – in the middle of the scrapbook, glued down tightly. You can see them there any time you go to tea with Jimmy and Susan!

The Little
Prickly Family

The Little
Prickly Family

ONCE UPON a time all the animals in Fir Tree Wood lived together in peace and happiness. There were the rabbits and the toads, the hedgehogs and the mice, the squirrels and the moles, and many others.

Then one day King Loppy, the sandy rabbit, sat down on what he thought was a brown heap of leaves – but it was Mr Prickles the hedgehog. He didn't like being sat on, and he stuck all his sharp spines upright, so that King Loppy jumped up with a shout of pain.

'How dare you prick the King of the Wood?' cried Loppy, standing his ears up straight in his anger. 'You did it on purpose!'

'No, I didn't, really,' said Mr Prickles. 'But it's not nice to be sat on quite so hard.'

'Well, I banish you from the wood!' said King Loppy, and he pointed with his paw towards the east, where the wood grew thinner. 'Go away at once, and take your horrid prickly family with you.'

Mr Prickles could do nothing else but obey. So sadly he went to fetch his wife and his six prickly children. They packed up all they owned, and walked out of Fir Tree Wood.

Now they hadn't been gone long when a family of red goblins came to the wood. They went to the Bluebell Dell, which was a pretty little hollow, and made their home there, right in the very middle of the wood.

At first the creatures of the wood took no notice, but soon the goblins made their lives so miserable that even King Loppy vowed he would turn the goblins out.

But he couldn't! The goblins knew too much magic,

and the animals were always afraid to say what they really thought for fear of being turned into mushrooms or earwigs. So they had to put up with their larders being raided each night, their firewood stolen, and their young ones frightened by the dreadful noises and ugly faces that the goblins made.

Once every month, when the moon was full, the goblins did a strange, barefoot dance in the dell. They danced round and round in the moonlight, holding hands and singing loud songs. All the animals were kept awake, and didn't they grumble – but not very loud, in case the red goblins heard and punished them.

'If anyone can get rid of these ugly red creatures for me, he shall be king instead of me!' declared Loppy one night. 'Our lives are a misery now, and these goblins must go!'

Well, a good many of the animals thought they would like to be king and wear the woodland crown, but try as they would, they couldn't think of a plan to make the goblins go.

Frisky the red squirrel wrote them a polite letter, and begged them to leave, but the only reply he had was to see all his nuts stolen one bright moonlight night.

Then Mowdie the mole wrote a very stern letter, and said that she would get a policeman from the world of humans, and have them all locked up, if they didn't go away, but they came and laughed so loudly at her that she shivered with fright and didn't go out shopping for three days.

Then bold Mr Hare marched right up to the goblins one day and ordered them out of the wood. He took a whip with him, and threatened to beat each goblin if they didn't obey him.

The goblins sat round and smiled. When Mr Hare tried to use his whip he found that he couldn't move! The goblins had used magic, and he was stuck fast to the ground! Then they tied him up to a birch tree all night long. Loppy found him the next morning, and Mr Hare vowed that he would never go near those horrid red goblins again!

After that no one did anything, till one day a letter came to Loppy from Mr Prickles the hedgehog. He opened it; and this is what it said:

Dear Your Majesty,

I think I can get rid of the goblins for you, but I do not want to be king. I only want to be allowed to come and live in Fir Tree Wood with all my friends once more. Please let me.

Your loving servant,
Prickles

When Loppy had read the letter he sat down and wrote an answer. This is what he said:

Dear Mr Prickles,

You may come back here to live if you can get rid of the goblins. But I don't believe you can.

Your loving king,
Loppy

When Mr Prickles got the letter he was overjoyed, for he felt certain he could get rid of the goblins. He looked up his calendar, and found that the next full-moon night was three nights ahead. On that night the red goblins would have their barefoot dance.

That day Mr Prickles went to see Tibbles the pixie, who was a great friend of his.

'I want you to do something for me,' he said. 'Will you go to the red goblins in Fir Tree Wood and tell them that someone has sent you to warn them against the magic pins and needles?'

'Goodness!' said Tibbles, with a laugh. 'What a funny message – and whatever are the pins and needles?'

'Never mind about that,' said Mr Prickles. 'You just go and give that message, there's a good pixie, and you can come back and have tea with us.'

So Tibbles set off to Bluebell Dell, and when he saw the red goblins he gave them the message.

'Someone has sent me to give you a warning,' he said, in a very solemn voice. 'You are to beware of the magic pins and needles.'

'Ooh!' said the goblins, looking scared. 'What are they? And what will they do? And who told you to warn us?'

'I can answer no questions,' said Tibbles, and he walked off, leaving the goblins wondering whatever the message meant.

Now, when the night of the full moon came, Mr Prickles and his wife and family made their way to Bluebell Dell. The red goblins were already beginning their barefoot dance. Their shoes and stockings were laid in a neat pile under a tree.

Without being seen, Mrs Prickles went to the pile, picked them up, and took them to the lily-pond not far off. She dropped all the shoes and stockings into the water, and then went back to her family.

'Are you all ready?' whispered Mr Prickles. 'Then – *roll*!'

With one accord all the hedgehogs curled themselves up tightly into balls, and rolled down the dell to the bottom where the goblins were busy dancing. They rolled all among their feet, and soon there was a terrible shouting and crying.

'Ooh! Ooh! I've trodden on a thorn! I've trodden on a prickle! Ooh! What's this!'

The hedgehogs rolled themselves in and out, and the goblins couldn't help treading on them. The prickles ran into their bare feet, and they hopped about in pain.

'What is it? What is it?' they cried, but at that moment the moon went in, and the goblins couldn't see anything. They just went on treading on the prickly hedgehogs, and cried out in pain and fright.

Then the head goblin suddenly gave a cry of dismay. 'It must be the magic pins and needles! It must be! We were warned against them, we were told to beware! Quick, put on your shoes and stockings before we get into their power!'

But the goblins couldn't find their pile of shoes and stockings – and no wonder, for they were all down at the bottom of the pond. They ran here and there looking for them, and Mr Prickles and his family rolled here and there after them. How those hedgehogs enjoyed themselves!

'The pins and needles have taken our shoes!' cried the goblins. 'Oh, oh, what shall we do? The pins and needles have found us!'

'Quick!' cried the head goblin. 'We must go back to Goblin Town and buy some more shoes for our feet. We must never come back here again!'

Off the goblins ran, as fast as they could, and the hedgehogs rolled after them. If any goblin stopped to take breath, he at once felt a prickly something on his foot, and he gave a cry of fright and ran on.

They made such a noise that all the wood animals came out to see what was the matter; and just then the moon shone out. The surprised animals saw the red goblins running for their lives, with the whole of the little prickly family of hedgehogs after them!

When the goblins were really gone, everyone crowded round the hedgehogs.

'You brave things to chase away those goblins!' cried Loppy the king. 'How could you dare to do such a thing! You are very plucky, Mr Prickles.'

'He shall be king!' shouted the animals.

'No,' said Mr Prickles, modestly. 'I am not great enough to be king. Loppy is far better than I am; but, please, Your Majesty, may I come back to live here, with all my prickly family?'

'Of course!' Loppy said gladly. 'But do tell me – how did you manage to chase the goblins away, Mr Prickles?'

'That is a secret,' said the hedgehog, and he wouldn't say another word.

Then he and all his prickly family came back to their home in the wood again and were very happy. Everyone praised them, and King Loppy had them to tea once a week, so you see he had quite forgiven

Mr Prickles for having pricked him when he sat down upon him.

As for the red goblins, they were never heard of again, but folk do say that whenever they think of that last moonlight night in Fir Tree Wood they get a funny feeling in their feet, and then they say:

'Ooh, I've got pins and needles!'

Have you ever felt that way, too?

They Said He
Was Too Small

They Said He Was Too Small

'CLEAR OFF!' yelled Dick to Joe. 'I've told you before, you're too small to play football with us!'

'I'm only a year younger than you!' yelled back Joe. 'And I'm a jolly good player, too!'

'You're not. You're too small to make a good footballer!' shouted Dick. 'You're a shrimp. Clear off!'

A boy near Joe gave him a shove. 'Go on – do what Dick says. He's the captain. We can't have tiddlers like you playing with us.'

'I can't help being small,' said Joe, angrily. 'I'll grow, won't I? Give me a chance. I've a big uncle who was a famous footballer, and I'm going to be like him. Give me a chance.'

But all he got was another shove which sent him flying to the ground. Joe got up and walked off crossly, wishing and wishing that he was as tall as the others.

He went home. His mother was surprised to see him. 'I thought you were playing football, Joe,' she said. 'Aren't the boys playing today?'

'Yes. But they told me to clear off,' said Joe, miserably. 'I'm too small. Can't I do anything to make myself grow, Mum? I'm a fast runner and a good kicker, and I just don't care how often I get tripped up.'

'Cheer up, Joe,' said his mother. 'I've some news for you. Uncle Jim is visiting Granny today. You know what a great footballer he was until he hurt his back. You go and talk to him about football. He'll tell you plenty of good tales.'

Joe sped off, thrilled. Uncle Jim had been such a

wonderful footballer! It would be marvellous to see him again and hear his tales. He might give Joe a few tips, too, on playing football.

Uncle Jim was at Granny's. Granny was his mother, and she was delighted to see him. She gave Joe a great welcome, too. 'Ah – my two footballers!' she said. 'Now, Jim, you just talk to Joe while I get the lunch.'

'Why aren't you out playing football this lovely Saturday morning?' asked Uncle Jim. 'I wouldn't have wasted a fine day like this when I was your age, if I could have been out on the football ground.'

'I feel like that, too,' said Joe. 'But the boys won't let me join their team. They say I'm a shrimp and a tiddler and much too small. All the same, I'm nearly as old as some of them.'

Uncle Jim saw that Joe was very miserable although he tried to smile. 'Never mind – we'll find one of my old footballs up in Granny's attic, and have a game to ourselves!' he said. So up he went and rummaged about, and soon came down again with a marvellous football. He made it ready for play and Joe looked on, excited. 'What is all this writing on the ball, Uncle?' he asked, running his finger over some faded words.

'Ah – those are the signatures of many famous footballers,' said his uncle. 'They gave me this football when I had to retire because of my back, and they signed their names on it. I think perhaps I'll give it to you, Joe – I shall never use it in a game again.'

Joe could hardly believe his ears. What! Have this magnificent football, with the autographs of famous footballers all over it! Why – goodness me – whatever would the boys say!

'Come on,' said Uncle Jim. 'We'll have a game and I'll give you a few hints. We'll have fun!'

They did have fun, and when Joe went home at lunchtime his face shone like the sun. He had had a wonderful morning – and now he owned a marvellous football! He would take it out to the field that very afternoon and kick it around.

So he went out that sunny afternoon and was soon kicking it round the field. Tom came up to him. 'That's a fine football. Where did you get it?'

'It belonged to my Uncle Jim – the one who was a footballer,' said Joe. 'And look – it has the autographs of all the famous players written on it. It's really too valuable to play with – but I simply must have a kick around!'

Tom went to find Dick, the captain. 'I say,' he said, 'that shrimp Joe has a simply magnificent football – look at it. It's much better than our old thing. It's got famous footballers' names signed all over it, too.'

'Go and ask him to join in our game, and see if he'll let us play with his football,' said Dick at once. So off went Tom back to Joe.

'Dick says you can play with us this afternoon – and bring that ball along with you,' he said.

'No thanks,' said Joe. 'I'm not big enough to play with you. You've said so dozens of times. I'll just kick it around by myself.'

Soon all the boys were watching Joe as he kicked the wonderful football about. 'Come on, Joe!' yelled John. 'Come and play. Let's have a kick at that ball.'

'I'm too small to play with you,' said Joe. 'You keep saying so. You only want me in because I've got this ball. And let me tell you this – my Uncle Jim played football with me this morning, and he gave me some good hints. I bet we'd win our next match if I told them to you.'

'You come on and play, Joe,' said Dick. 'We do want your ball, it's true – but if you play well, we'll want you too. Come on – we're a boy short.'

Joe grinned. He had meant to play all the time. He kicked the ball to Dick. 'All right,' he said. 'I'll make a bargain with you. If I play well you'll let me into the team with my ball. But if I've told a fib, and I play badly, well, kick me out – but I'll still lend you my ball. How's that?'

'You're a good littl'un,' said Dick, and gave him a

slap on the back. 'Right. It's a bargain!'

Well, you should have seen Joe that afternoon. He ran like a hare. He shot two goals. He took the ball from the other side time after time. He tried out all the tricks his uncle had shown him. He fell heavily at least six times but he was up and running again at once. And how marvellous that ball was compared with the old one the boys had played with for weeks!

The game was over at last. The boys clustered round Joe, panting. Dick gave him such a slap on the back that the small boy almost fell over.

'You win, Joe! You're in the team. You may be a tiddler, but, my word, you're a good tiddler! We can do with someone like you!'

'You're sure I'm not too small for you?' said Joe, slyly.

'We're sure – so long as you're sure we're not too big for you!' said Dick. 'You go along and tell your uncle we like his ball – and we like his nephew even better!'

Well, wasn't that good? Joe's grown up now and he's a wonderful footballer. You've read his name in the paper many a time!

When the Moon Was Blue

When the Moon Was Blue

ONE EVENING, when Jack and Mary were going to bed, they forgot to clean their teeth.

Their mother saw their toothbrushes lying beside their toothmugs and called to them:

'You naughty children! You haven't cleaned your teeth!'

'We forgot!' said Jack, and the two ran to get their brushes. 'Have you ever forgotten to clean your teeth, Mummy?'

'Oh, I dare say I have,' said Mummy.

'How often?' asked Mary.

'Oh, once in a blue moon!' said their mother,

drawing the curtains back so that the air could come into the room.

'What's a blue moon?' said Jack.

'I really don't know,' said Mother. 'Just an ordinary moon turned blue, I expect. I've never seen one.'

'You often say things happen "once in a blue moon",' said Mary. 'But a blue moon never comes.'

'Well – it might some day!' laughed Mother. 'You'd better be careful then – for goodness knows what might happen if the moon turned blue!'

The children got into bed. Mother kissed them and said good night. Then she turned out the light and went downstairs.

'It's very light outside tonight,' said Mary. 'The moon must be up.'

'Daddy said it would be a full moon tonight,' said Jack. 'Oh, Mary – wouldn't it be exciting if it was blue!'

'Yes – but it won't be,' said Mary sleepily. 'Things like that never seem to happen. Think how often we've tried to see fairies, and never have, and how often we've wished wishes and they haven't come true, and tried to work spells and they won't work. I don't believe in those things any more!'

'I still do,' said Jack, 'because once one of my wishes really did come true.'

'Well, it must have been an accident, then,' said Mary, yawning. 'Goodnight, Jack. I'm going to sleep.'

Both children fell fast asleep in a minute or two. They slept soundly, and didn't hear the wardrobe creaking loudly. They didn't hear the cat mewing outside.

But when twelve o'clock struck, they did hear something. At least, Jack did. He heard an owl hooting outside the window, and he opened his eyes.

'Wit-wit!' said the owl. 'Woo-wit-wit!'

Jack sat up and wondered what time it was. He looked at the window. A good deal of light came in from outside, for the moon was full. It had gone behind a cloud for a moment, quite a small one, for

Jack could see the moon behind it. He watched it, waiting for it to come out again.

And when it did he gasped and stared and rubbed his eyes – for what do you suppose? Why, the big round moon was as blue as forget-me-nots! There it shone in the sky, looking very peculiar indeed.

'There's a blue moon!' cried Jack. 'Mary, Mary, wake up! There's a blue moon!'

Mary woke up with a jump and sat up. She stared at the moon in the greatest surprise.

'So there is!' she said. 'Oh, Jack – do you suppose anything extraordinary will happen? Oh, do let's go to the window and see if we can see any fairies or pixies about. Mummy said we might see them once in a blue moon!'

They ran to the window – and looked down the moonlit garden. But not a fairy or pixie could they see.

'Let's wish a few wishes,' said Jack, gazing up at the bright blue moon. 'They might come true now the moon is blue.'

'Yes, let's,' said Mary. 'I wish we could see a fairy or a gnome or something!'

'And I wish we could too!' said Jack.

And immediately they did! A gnome, very small and bent, ran out from under the lilac bush in the middle of the garden, and went to the little round pond. In the middle of this was a little statue of a rabbit, sitting on a big flat stone.

The gnome jumped over the water and landed beside the rabbit. At once the stone rabbit took his hand, and stood up. The gnome began to pull at the flat stone on which the rabbit had been sitting – and before the children's very eyes, he suddenly disappeared! The stone rabbit sat down again and made no more movement.

'Did you see that, Mary?' cried Jack. 'Come on, quickly! We'll see where he disappeared to. Put on your dressing gown and I'll put on mine.'

They threw on their dressing gowns and ran quietly down the stairs. Out they went into the garden and ran to the pond. With a leap Jack was over the water and standing beside the stone rabbit in the middle of the pond. To his enormous surprise, the small rabbit at once put a cold paw into his hand and got up. Jack turned to the flat stone – and saw an iron ring on it, just where the rabbit had sat. He pulled at it and the stone came up. Under it lay a steep stone stairway!

'Come on, Mary!' cried Jack. 'Here's an adventure for us! We've always wanted one!'

Mary jumped over the water beside Jack and peered down the steps. The stone rabbit put its other paw into her hand, and looked beseechingly at her.

'This little rabbit's alive, although it's just a statue!' said Mary, in surprise. 'Can you speak, Bunny?'

'Yes,' said the rabbit. 'I can speak, once in a blue moon – and the moon is blue tonight!'

'Are you really a statue or are you alive?' asked Jack.

'I was once the first rabbit in the carriage of the

Princess Philomela of Heyho Land,' said the rabbit. 'But one night the wicked gnome Twisty lay in wait for her carriage – and put a log in our path. So over I went and all the other three rabbits, and the Princess fell out of the carriage. The gnome picked her up and carried her off – and turned me and the other rabbits into stone. He sold us for the middles of ponds and there we stayed!'

'Goodness me!' said Jack, in the greatest surprise. 'Whoever would have thought of such a thing? Where is the Princess now?'

'I don't know,' said the rabbit, mournfully. 'Still a prisoner somewhere, I expect. The gnome has a secret way to Fairyland down that stairway. He may have gone to the Princess now.'

'Well, let's go after him then!' said Jack. 'We may see where he keeps the Princess, and perhaps be able to rescue her! Will you come with us, Bunny?'

'Yes, but I'm made of stone, and I would make so much noise!' said the rabbit.

'I'll wish you alive again!' said Jack. 'It seems as if wishes come true in a blue moon!'

'Yes, wish!' said Mary. So Jack wished hard.

'I wish this stone bunny may come alive!' he said, and immediately his wish came true! The little rabbit grew soft and warm and furry – and whiskers grew out of his cheeks. The stone rabbit had had no whiskers at all.

'I'm alive, I'm alive!' he cried, frisking round and nearly falling into the pond.

'Mind! You'll fall in the water!' said Mary, clutching hold of the excited bunny. 'Come along. We'll go down the steps now.'

So down the steps they all went, Jack first, then the bunny, then Mary. It was dark when they got to the bottom, but a lamp hung a little way farther on, and showed them a narrow passage. They went along, most excited.

After a while they came to a turnstile, and they pushed against it. It wouldn't turn round, and Jack thought they had better climb over it. But before he could do so a small brownie popped his head out of a window in the wall of the passage and said, 'Penny each, please.'

'We haven't any pennies,' said Jack. 'We are in our dressing gowns, and we don't keep pennies there. Please let us through. Has the gnome Twisty gone this way?'

'Yes, he has,' said the brownie, nodding his head. 'He often goes this way. No one else goes except myself – and I only go once in a blue moon!'

'Well, it's a blue moon tonight!' said Jack. 'We've seen it!'

'What!' cried the brownie, his face full of excitement. 'The moon is blue! My stars, I must go and look!'

He squeezed himself through the window in the wall of the passage, pushed past Jack, Mary and the rabbit, and disappeared up the tunnel.

'Come on, let's climb over, now he's gone!' said

Mary. So they all climbed over the turnstile, and went on down the tunnel again. But it didn't go very far this time. It opened out into a cave through which a dark, swift river ran. A little pixie sat by the side of some boats, half asleep.

'Wake up!' cried Jack, running to him. 'Has the gnome Twisty gone this way?'

'Yes, down the river,' said the pixie, in surprise. 'But he said I was to let no one else but him have my boats today.'

'Oh, well, it can't matter once in a blue moon!' said Jack, getting into one.

'What, is the moon blue?' cried the pixie, in delight. 'Oh, have my boats then – have them all if you want to! I'm going up to see the moon, the moon, the moon!'

He sat down on a big toadstool growing nearby and, to the children's great amazement, shot upwards at a great speed.

'Well, I suppose he's gone to see the moon, like

the brownie,' said Jack. 'Come on, Mary and Bunny! We mustn't let the gnome Twisty get too far ahead.'

They set off in a boat. Jack steered, but there was no need for oars, for the river was very strong and took them along itself. In a few minutes it came out into the open air, and there, hanging in the sky, was the moon, still as blue as forget-me-nots!

As the boat went along, Jack caught sight of a large notice on one of the banks. He looked at it. To his great surprise, it had one word on it:

JUMP!

'Jump,' said Jack puzzled. 'Why jump?'

'Oh, look!' cried Mary, pointing ahead. 'There's a waterfall or something coming. Jack, if we don't jump, we shall go over the falls. Oh, I'm frightened!'

'Come with me,' the rabbit said. He took the strings from Jack and steered the boat towards the bank. It ran into it with a bump, and at the same time all three jumped out! They landed on the soft grass and rolled over. Just ahead of them the river shot over the falls with a roar. Their boat spun round once and then headed for the waterfall. Over it went, and that was the last they saw of it!

'Goodness! I hope this sort of thing only happens once in a blue moon!' said Jack.

'Oh, it does,' said the rabbit. 'Come on. Do you see that castle over there? I am sure that is where the gnome has gone. It belongs to him. Perhaps he has the Princess Philomela locked up in one of the rooms.'

They all set off for the castle. They soon arrived there, and looked up at it. It was very big, and had hundreds of shining windows, and a great wooden door.

'I don't think I want to go in that door,' said Mary. 'It looks as if it might shut behind us and make us prisoners in the castle too. Isn't there another way of getting in?'

'We'll spy round and see,' said Jack. So they walked

all round the castle and right at the back they discovered a very small door, painted a bright yellow. Jack pushed it – and it came open!

He and the others peeped inside. It led into a great yard. They all went inside, and looked round. The kitchen door stood open and a smell of cakes being baked came out.

'Come on,' said Jack. 'We may be able to sneak inside.'

He crept up to the kitchen door – and at that very moment a large gnome-woman came to it to shake a duster. She stared at the three in surprise. They didn't know what to say.

'Oh,' she said at last, 'I suppose you have come with a message for Twisty the gnome. You are not the washing, are you? Or the baker?'

'Oh, no,' said Jack. 'May we go inside and see the gnome?'

Mary was horrified to hear Jack ask this, for she certainly didn't want to see the horrid gnome Twisty, in case they were all taken prisoner. The gnome servant nodded her head.

'He's just upstairs with the Princess,' she said. 'But he won't be long. Come and wait in the hall.'

She took them inside and led them to a great hall. They sat down on a bench and she disappeared back into the kitchen.

'Did you hear that?' said Jack, in excitement. 'She said the gnome Twisty was upstairs with the Princess! So she is here! We'll rescue her! Come on – we must hide before the gnome comes back. I don't want to see him, of course – that was only an excuse to get inside!'

Jack, Mary and the rabbit looked round to see where they could hide. There was a long curtain hanging at the foot of the stairs, and the three crept behind it. They hadn't been there more than a minute or two when they heard footsteps coming down the stairs. It was the gnome Twisty.

As he came into the hall, the gnome-woman ran out. 'Master,' she said, 'there are three . . .'

She stopped short and looked round in surprise – for she could not see Mary, Jack or the rabbit. 'How strange!' she said. 'A boy and a girl and a rabbit came to see you. They were here just now!'

'Oh, indeed!' said Twisty, in a hoarse and threatening voice. 'They were here, were they? Well, where are they now? I suppose you've let them go into my magic room, and disturb my spells. Grrrrrr! If you have, I'll turn you into a dustbin lid. That's all you're fit for!'

'Oh, Master, I don't think they've gone into your magic room!' cried the servant – but the gnome had disappeared into a little room on the opposite side of the hall. The servant followed – and in a second Mary, Jack and the rabbit had slipped out from the curtain and were running upstairs as fast as they could!

At each landing they found locked doors. Jack stopped outside each one and called softly.

'Princess Philomela! Are you there?'

But there was no reply at all until he reached the

topmost room of all – and then an answer came, in a soft, eager voice.

'Yes, yes! I am here! Who is it?'

The door was locked and bolted but the key was in the lock. Jack turned it, and then undid the bolts. He opened the door and saw inside the room a beautiful little princess with long golden hair waving round her face, and the brightest blue eyes he had ever seen.

'Oh, oh, you've come to rescue me!' cried Philomela, and she gave Jack and Mary a tight hug each. She saw the rabbit and clapped her hands in delight.

'Why, you are dear little Whiskers, one of the bunnies that used to pull my carriage!' she said, and she lifted him up and kissed him. 'I suppose you brought these children here to save me.'

'We must go, Princess,' said Jack. 'The gnome knows we are here. He is looking for us downstairs. He may come up at any minute.'

'Come along then,' said Philomela.

So they all began to creep down the stairs and

at last came to the hall. No one was there. Not a sound was to be heard. Every door that led into the hall was shut.

'I say!' said Jack. 'I don't remember which door led into the kitchen, do you?'

'We don't need to go that way,' said Mary. 'What about trying the front door?'

'No,' said Jack. 'It's too big and heavy. It would make a noise. Let's go into one of the rooms – it doesn't matter which one so long as the gnome isn't there – and then climb out of the window. That should be easy.'

So they listened outside the nearest door and, not hearing the tiniest sound from inside, they pushed open the door and slipped into the room. They ran to some curtains and pulled them aside to get at the windows – but alas – there were no windows at all!

Then they heard the sound of a key being turned in the lock – and looked round to see Twisty the gnome looking at them with a very nasty grin.

'Ha!' he said. 'So you thought you would rescue the Princess and all escape very nicely, did you? Well, you made a mistake, I'm afraid. I have four prisoners now, instead of one!'

He went to the middle of the floor, and pulled up a small wooden trapdoor.

'Get down into my cellar,' he said. 'There is no escape from there. It is dark and cold and full of spiders. You will enjoy a night or two there, I am sure!'

The Princess and Mary began to cry. Jack looked fierce but could do nothing. The rabbit slipped down into the cellar without a word.

When they were all in the dark, damp cellar, the gnome shut the trapdoor with a bang and bolted it. They heard his footsteps going out of the room above.

'Oh dear! What are we to do?' sobbed Philomela. 'Oh, I am so frightened.'

'So am I!' said Mary, wiping her eyes.

'There's no need to be,' said the rabbit, in a soft

voice. 'I can rescue you all. I am a bunny, you know, and my paws are good for digging holes. This cellar is in the ground; there is earth all around. It will not take me long to dig my way out and then I will fetch many more rabbits and we will all dig together.'

'Splendid idea!' cried Jack. The rabbit at once began to scrape in the earth. Soon he had made quite a tunnel, and the earth was piled in the cellar. In a few minutes he had disappeared – and before long he had fetched fifteen more rabbits, who all dug and scraped away valiantly.

'Now I think the tunnel is big enough,' said the rabbit. And so it was. Jack, Mary and Philomela easily made their way up it, and came out at the side of the big castle!

'The rabbits have brought a carriage for you, Your Highness,' said the little rabbit – and there, sure enough, was a shining silver carriage! Four rabbits stood ready to pull it, and the Princess got in.

'You must come too,' she said to the children,

but just as they were about to get in, a peculiar thing happened.

'Look at the moon!' cried the rabbit, and pointed to where the moon was slowly sinking down in the sky.

Everyone looked. It was turning bright yellow! Yes – there was no mistake about it. All its blue colour was fading, and even as they watched, it was all gone, and there was the moon, as bright yellow as a daffodil, filling the sky with light.

'The blue moon's gone,' said the rabbit sadly. 'It's gone – but we've rescued the Princess!'

A strange wind blew up at that moment and the children suddenly felt giddy. There came a loud humming noise. Jack and Mary sat down on the grass and shut their eyes, for they felt very peculiar.

After a while the humming noise died away and they opened their eyes.

Will you believe it? – they were back in their beds again! Yes, they were, both of them sitting up and gazing out of the window at the moon, which was yellow, and shining brightly!

'Mary!' cried Jack. 'Did we dream it all?'

'No, we couldn't have,' said Mary. 'It was all so real. The moon really was blue!'

'Well, tomorrow we will look for that trapdoor again, where the bunny was,' said Jack, lying down. 'Then we will know for certain it was all true. How funny – Daddy will wonder where the stone bunny has gone, won't he?'

But do you know, when the morning came, the stone rabbit was back again. Yes, he was sitting in the middle of the pond on the big flat stone, just as before.

'But the trapdoor is underneath him, Daddy,' said Mary, earnestly, after she had told her father all about their very strange adventure. 'It really is. Will you take him off the stone and see?'

'No,' said Father. 'He is cemented to the stone. I'm not going to move him. You dreamed it all!'

Well, isn't that a pity? If only their father would move the rabbit and let the children find that trapdoor again, they would know it wasn't a dream. But he won't.

Perhaps you will see a blue moon one day. If you do, wish a wish – for it is sure to come true, once in a blue moon!

The Bumblebee
Hums

The Bumblebee
Hums

ALL THE hedgerow folk liked to hear the humming of the bees. It was a summery sound, lazy and warm. The earliest bees had been abroad in March, seeking for the flowers that opened on the bank below. More bees had come in April, and very soon there had been heard the loud booming of the big brown and yellow bumble-bee. She *did* make a noise. Zooooooooom! Zooooooooom! It was a lovely droning sound, never heard in the cold days of winter.

The bumblebee had slept all through the winter in a little hole on the north side of the hedgerow-bank. It was a cold hole, full of bitterness when the north winds blew in January and February. But the bumblebee had chosen it carefully. She knew that to choose a warm hole on the south side of the hedge would be dangerous. The sun came early to the south bank, and sent its warm beams into every nook and cranny there, waking up all the small sleepers. But to wake up on a sunny day in February and crawl forth might mean death when the frost returned at night. It was best to sleep in a cold place, unwarmed by the early sunshine of the year, and not to wake until all fear of frosts was past.

The bumblebee had carefully made a honeypot for herself before going to sleep. Then, if by chance she should awake, she could have a sip of honey from her pot and need not run the risk of leaving her hole. The hole was small. It had been made by a worm, and the bee squatted down in the enlarged room at the end of the hole, her honeypot beside her. She did not wake until February, and then although the sun was shining warmly on the south side of the hedge, her hole was still rimmed around by frost and she did not stir out. She sipped her honey and went to sleep again.

At last, on a warm spring day, she walked out, feeling rather top-heavy and a little dazed with her long, cold sleep. She spread her wings and the hedgerow heard once again the loud booming hum that it liked so much in the summertime. The warm days must be coming if the bumblebee was about!

The bee decided to look for a new hole – a warm one this time, and a bigger one. She knew the hedgerow well, and thought it would be good to find one there, for then she would not need to learn new surroundings. So she began her hunt.

There was one rather big hole on the south side, but the bumblebee came out quickly after one look, for a most enormous spider lived there! She looked under an old stone and saw a fat toad peering at her with gleaming eyes. He knew she was dangerous and did not flick out his tongue to eat her. She backed out quickly. Then she flew to another part of the bank, humming busily, enjoying herself in the hot sun. And at last she found exactly the right hole!

It had been made by mice, and their smell still hung about the little hole. The bumblebee altered the hole to her liking and then fetched in some moss. She crawled out again and brought back some grass. Then she visited some flowers and returned with pollen which she packed into the hole. She looked at the heap of moss, grass and pollen, and decided it was time to lay her eggs.

So she built some egg cells and put pollen into each. Then she laid her eggs, one in each cell – white, long-shaped eggs that she loved very much. She spread herself over them to brood them. By her were several of her honeypots, full of honey. She was glad when her eggs hatched out into grubs – but how hungry they were! They soon ate up all the pollen in their cells, and the bumblebee knew they were hungry. So in each cell she bit a tiny hole, and passed more food through to her growing children.

Now the big bumblebee was busy all day long. She went out to find food for her first batch of children; she laid more eggs; she built more and more cells; she taught the first batch of young bees how to help her. She was happy, and the hedgerow liked to hear her going booming about her work.

One morning she heard the loud humming of another creature nearby, and she stopped in her flight to see who it was. It was a large queen wasp, and the bumblebee was interested to see that she was doing exactly what she herself had done some weeks before – she was hunting for a hole in the bank!

'You are late in finding a home,' boomed the big bumblebee.

'I only awake when the sun has plenty of warmth in it,' buzzed the wasp. 'All the winter I slept in a hidden cranny behind an ivy-root in the hedge. A little mouse once woke me up when he came hunting for the nuts the squirrel hid, but he soon fled when he saw *me*!'

'*I* have a fine nest in an old mouse-hole,' hummed

the bee, settling down beside the big queen wasp. 'Come and see it.'

But the wasp was in a hurry. She was anxious to find a hole for herself and begin her building. The summer would soon be here and she must lay her eggs. She ran to a hole and crawled inside to see if it would suit her. But a big beetle was there, and showed her his great, ugly jaws. The wasp hurried out again and flew to another hole. This was too big, and full of rubbish.

At last she found exactly what she needed. This was an old tunnel made by the mole the summer before. Part of the roof had fallen in at the back. The wasp walked all over the hole, touching the walls with her feelers. This was a good place. She was pleased with it. She crawled up to the roof and found there the root of a hawthorn bush jutting out. She could hang her nest from that.

She left the hole and flew up into the air, circling round as she did so, noticing everything round her hole – the stone nearby – the tuft of grass – the thistle

– all these things would help her to know her hole again. Then she flew higher still into the air, and noticed bigger things – the near-by ditch, the hedgerow itself, the big bramble-spray that waved high in the air. Ah, she would know her way back again now!

The queen wasp was going to build a city and be its ruler. She was going to have thousands of subjects, who would work for her night and day. She was longing to begin, for the warm sun had heated her blood and given her strength and joy.

She flew off to the common up on the hill, and looked about her as she went. She was hunting for a piece of oak from which she could take a scraping to start her city. She found a gatepost and settled down on it. She bit a piece of wood out, a mere shaving, with her strong jaws. She chewed it and chewed it until it was paper-pulp. Then back she flew to the hole she had taken for her own. She crawled in – and immediately began a fierce buzzing, for there were three ants there! She drove her sting into each one and threw them out of the hole, little curled-up brown things, poisoned by her sting.

She stuck the paper pellet to the root at the top of the hole and then went off for more. In and out she flew all day long, building the roof of her house first, for the wasp-people live in topsy-turvy homes! Every time she left the hole she carried with her a pellet of earth, for she wanted to have plenty of room for her city.

She often met the big bumblebee, who told her that she had now plenty of workers to help her, for many of her grubs had grown into bees, and did her work.

'Come and play for a while,' said the bumblebee. 'The fields are full of flowers.'

'I have no use for flowers,' said the wasp, impatiently. 'Leave me, cousin. I am too busy. I have many things to do, and I have as yet no helpers as you have! What there is to be done I do myself.'

Soon there was a pile of earth outside the old mole-hole, and inside, built safely under an umbrella-like covering of grey paper, were many wasp-cells, each containing a small grub. They hung head downwards in their cells, and were tightly glued to the top so that they could not fall out of the hole at the bottom. Soon they grew large and fat, and were so wedged in that they could not have fallen out if they had wanted to.

Then each grub spun a silk sheet over the cell-opening and formed a cocoon. The queen wasp waited impatiently for them to come forth from their cells, and at last the time came. Each little wasp bit through its cell and came out. They cleaned themselves up, and then looked round the nest. Very soon they were helping the queen wasp, their mother, to do the tasks she had done for some weeks alone.

They helped to feed the new grubs. They cleaned the nest – and then one morning, when the sun came right into the hole, the young wasps went to the opening and looked out. What a glorious world of light and warmth! They spread out their shining wings and flew into the air, each small wasp taking careful notice of all the things around their hole so that they would know the way back, and would not get lost. Then off they went, all knowing exactly what to do, although they had never done their new tasks before.

Some of them found the old oak post from which their mother had scraped shavings to make the paper-pulp she used in building her city. They too took scrapings and chewed them into pulp, taking the pellets home again to build on to their nest, which was now three storeys high. Other wasps went to a sunny wall on which many flies crawled. They caught the flies, cut off their wings, heads and legs, and carried them back to the nest to feed the young grubs. One wasp found a hiding place in which four moths crouched and, cutting off their wings, carried the bodies away for food. They were all busy, all happy.

They had their enemies, and so had the young bumblebees, who were also helping their mother in the nest. The spotted flycatcher had come back from its winter haunts and darted at the passing bees and wasps, as well as at the flies. Even the queen wasp herself had a narrow escape one day. The great tit too would sometimes wait outside the hole where the bumblebee had her nest, and would pounce on an unwary bee just leaving.

One day all the bees and the wasps heard a strange noise. It was a high humming, very shrill and loud, like a wasp or bee army on the march. Every wasp and every bumblebee flew to see what it was – and they saw a strange sight! A great cloud of honeybees was coming over the field towards the hedgerow. It was led by the queen bee, and thousands of bees were following her. The queen wasp flew near and demanded to know what had happened, for she was excited and half-frightened by the tremendous humming.

'We come from a hive far away,' boomed the queen honeybee. 'I had so many worker bees that the hive became too small. So I have brought half the hive away with me and I am looking for a new home. I have left behind me some princesses in the hive. One of them will become queen in my place.'

'*We* do not swarm!' said the queen wasp. 'I make my city as big as I want it.'

'You are only a wasp!' buzzed the honeybee. 'Your city will crumble to nothing in the autumn; all your people will die! But my people live with me, for we store up honey for the cold days!'

The wasp shivered. She thought of the days to come when the frost would creep on her again – when her people would freeze and die – her beautiful city be eaten by hungry mice! But what did she care? *She* would live! Next spring she would come forth again and once more build a marvellous city. She buzzed happily and flew off to her hole. The swarm settled on the lowest branch of the oak-tree, and then in a short while flew off again, no one knew where.

'Zooooooooom!' buzzed the bumblebee to the queen wasp. 'Who would be a hive bee and live in slavery? Not I! Give me a hole in a bank and let me be my own mistress! Zooooooooom!'

Andrew's Robin

Andrew's Robin

IN ANDREW'S garden there was a robin which he called his own. It was a black-eyed, long-legged, red-breasted little bird, so tame that it would take a bit of biscuit from Andrew's fingers.

That summer the robin had built its nest in an old saucepan under the hedge. Andrew remembered putting the saucepan there when he played house, and he had forgotten to take it away. The robin found it, and he and his little mate had put a cosy nest there.

Andrew was pleased. He watched the robins going to and from the nest. He saw the five eggs they laid there. He even saw three of the eggs hatch out. That was exciting. The tiny birds inside the eggs pecked at the shell and broke it. Then out they came – bare black babies without a single feather on them.

The next day all five eggs had hatched. The robins threw the empty shells out of the saucepan nest and began hunting for caterpillars and grubs to feed their five hungry babies.

'That will keep you busy,' said Andrew as he peeped at the five tiny birds, all with their beaks wide open. 'When I dig my garden I will hunt for caterpillars too, and bring them to you.'

One day a dreadful thing happened to the robins. A grey squirrel came that way and saw the nest in the saucepan. Now the grey squirrel liked, for a change, to make a meal of baby birds, so when he saw the little robins he ran over to them at once.

The father and mother robin were not there as they had gone hunting for grubs. The squirrel picked up two of the tiny creatures in his mouth and ran off with them.

How those babies squeaked! The father and mother robin heard them at once and came flying back. When they saw the grey squirrel they knew quite well what he had been up to and they flew at him, singing loudly in anger, for that is the way of robins.

The squirrel stopped. One robin flew at his right eye and the other flew at his left. He shook his head. He dodged. But it was no use. Those robins would not leave him alone until he dropped the baby birds.

So the grey squirrel dropped them on the lawn and then bounded off to a tree. Up he went and sat there making faces at the robins.

The robins flew down to their two frightened babies. They were not really hurt – but they could not possibly get back to the nest themselves.

'We must carry them in our beaks,' sang the mother robin. But alas! The babies were too heavy.

'Leave them, leave them!' sang the freckled thrush. 'I don't bother about my young ones if they fall from the nest.'

But the robins were not like the thrush. They would not leave their little ones. But what could they do? The babies were too heavy to carry.

'Fetch Andrew, fetch Andrew!' sang the father robin. 'He is kind and strong.'

So the robins went to fetch Andrew. He was in his room, building a big castle, and was very surprised to see the two robins fly in at the window. The father robin flew to the top of Andrew's big castle and sang loudly to him. Andrew stared at him. The robin flew to the window and back again.

'What is it you want?' asked Andrew, puzzled. The robin sang again and flew to the windowsill. Andrew got up and went too – and he saw something on the lawn. What could it be?

He ran downstairs and out into the garden. As soon as he came to the baby birds, lying helpless on the grass, he guessed why the robins had come to him.

'They want me to put their babies back,' said Andrew in delight. 'Oh, the clever little things! They knew I would help them.'

He gently lifted the two frightened baby birds and

took them to the nest in the saucepan. He put them with the others and they soon settled down happily.

'Thank you!' sang the robins. 'You are kind!'

The robins were afraid of the squirrel after that. Always one of them stayed to guard the nest until the babies were too big to be taken away by a squirrel. Soon they could fly. Soon they had flown. The little robin family split up and they all left the garden, except for the father robin. This little bird stayed there with Andrew, singing to him as he played in the garden. He never once forgot how kind the little boy had been to the baby birds.

One day Andrew took his clockwork train and railway lines on to the lawn. He set the train going and had a wonderful time with it. When it was teatime he had to pack it up in a hurry and go in, and it wasn't till the next day that he found he had lost the key of his beautiful clockwork engine.

'Oh, Mummy, now I can't play with my engine any more, because the key is lost,' he said. 'I have hunted everywhere in the garden, but I can't find it. I am so unhappy.'

The robin heard him. He had seen Andrew winding up the engine. He guessed what the key was – that little shiny thing. He began to hunt for it.

And at last he found it. No wonder Andrew couldn't see it, for it was halfway down a worm's burrow. The robin pulled it out. It was a bit rusty, but it was the lost key, no doubt about that.

The robin took it in his beak and flew to Andrew's playroom. He sat on the windowsill and made a little creamy sound, for he couldn't sing very loudly with something in his beak. Andrew looked up.

'Oh!' he cried in great delight. 'You've found my key! You dear, good little bird! Thank you so much!'

'You helped me, and I helped you!' carolled the robin. 'That is as it should be. Soon it will be wintertime, Andrew. Help me again and give me crumbs.'

'I will, I will!' promised Andrew. And I know he will keep his promise.

The Two Cross Boys

The Two Cross Boys

TOM AND WILLIE were cousins. Sometimes they went to stay with one another, and that was fun – at least, it would have been fun if they hadn't quarrelled so much!

The worst of it was that when they quarrelled they wouldn't make it up, and, of course, that's very silly. But Tom's mother cured them, as you will see.

Willie went to stay with Tom, and for the first two days they had a good time. Tom was so pleased to have Willie to play with that he let him have all his toys.

'You can ride my bicycle if you like!' he said. 'You

can use my skateboard when you want to. You can climb that tree down there in the garden that I call my very own.'

'Thank you, Tom,' said Willie, and he rode the bicycle, used the skateboard, and climbed the tree.

And then, after two days, they quarrelled. Quarrels are often about silly little things that don't really matter at all, and this one was so silly that you will hardly believe it.

Tom hit his elbow hard against the wall and it hurt him. The tears came into his eyes. Willie saw what he had done and he laughed.

'You shouldn't cry, Tom,' he said, 'you should laugh! That was your funny-bone you hit against the wall.'

'It was not a funny bone at all,' said Tom, who didn't know that we call the point of our elbow our funny-bone. 'It wasn't a bit funny. It was horrid. I'm hurt.'

'Well, if you won't laugh at your funny-bone,

I shall!' said Willie teasingly. 'Ha ha ha! Ho ho ho!'

'You horrid thing!' said Tom angrily. 'You shouldn't laugh when people are hurt. I shan't speak to you!'

'Funnier than ever,' said Willie. 'Ha ha ha! Ho ho ho!'

Tom slapped him. Willie slapped back. Then they both yelled at the tops of their voices, for Tom had slapped Willie on the cheek and Willie had slapped Tom on the nose, and both places hurt.

Tom's mother came hurrying out. 'Now, now,' she said, 'quarrelling again! I did think that this time you were old enough to play nicely together. Now, make up your quarrel, and then go and play football in the field, for a treat.'

'I don't want to,' said Tom, and he turned away.

'I shall never speak to Tom again,' said Willie, as Tom marched off with his hands in his pockets, and his nose looking quite red from the slap it had received.

Tom's mother went indoors again, thinking what little sillies the two boys were. 'I expect they'll soon get over it,' she thought.

But, you know, they didn't! They wouldn't smile at one another or speak to each other all day. They wouldn't say good night at night. They wouldn't sit next to each other at breakfast time the next morning. It was very unpleasant for Tom's mother, for she did like smiling faces and happy talk.

'What are you going to do this morning?' she asked.

'Well, if Tom's going to be in the garden I shall be indoors,' said Willie sulkily.

'And if Willie's in the house I shall be outside,' said Tom at once.

'You are both very silly, stupid boys,' said Tom's mother. 'You are wasting all the time you have together just because you can't make up a quarrel about Tom's funny-bone.'

'I'll do any jobs for you, Auntie,' said Willie, feeling a bit ashamed of himself. 'Give me some work to do and you'll soon see I'm not stupid.'

'If anybody's going to do a job for my mother, I'm going to do it!' said Tom at once.

'Well, you shall both do a job for me,' said Tom's mother, and she smiled a funny little secret smile to herself.

'What is the job?' asked Tom.

'I want the big kitchen window cleaned,' said Tom's mother.

'Well, Mum, I said if Willie's in the house I shall be out-of-doors,' said Tom. 'I won't work in the same place with him.'

'Very well,' said his mother. 'Tom, you shall clean the inside of the window and Willie shall clean the outside. I've got two window cloths, so that will be all right.'

In a little while the boys went to do their job. Each had a window cloth and some cleaner. Tom was to do the inside, and Willie was to do the outside of the window. Each of them was quite determined to do his side better than the other.

They began. They wouldn't look at one another, but Tom thought it would be fun to pretend to rub out Willie's red face. So he rubbed hard with his cloth just where Willie's face was. And then Willie guessed what he was doing, and he decided he would rub out Tom's face!

So he ducked down to see Tom's face, and then began to try to rub him out through the glass!

Now you can't do things like this without feeling rather giggly. It's funny to begin with, to rub away so near to one another, with only the window in between – and it's funnier still if you are cross and try to rub someone out!

Then the boys found that their hands were rubbing in time, together – forward, back, one, two; forward, back, one, two! Then they rubbed fiercely at one another's hands – and then they caught one another's eye, and found that each had a little twinkle in it!

'I shan't look at him,' thought Tom. 'If I do I know I shall laugh.'

'I won't even peep at him!' said Willie to himself. 'I feel as if I shall giggle if I do!'

But they did keep looking at one another just to see if the other was smiling – and soon Tom's mouth curled itself upwards, and he had to hide it in his handkerchief. Then Willie felt as if he was going to giggle, swallowed the giggle and choked and spluttered till he was scarlet in the face!

He looked so funny that Tom began to giggle too. He tried to stop. He shut his mouth. Another giggle burst out of it. He ran away to a corner of the room, put his head into a cushion and laughed till the tears came out of his eyes and trickled down the cushions.

Willie peeped through the window and saw what Tom was doing, and that made him laugh too. He sat on the windowsill and roared with laughter.

Tom's mother heard them and looked into the room. 'Whatever are you laughing at, Tom?' she asked.

'Oh, Mum, it's so funny to clean a window with

somebody else cleaning it outside,' said Tom. 'I just can't help laughing.'

Tom's mother went outside. 'What are you laughing at, Willie?' she said.

'Oh, Auntie, you should have seen Tom and me cleaning this window together!' he giggled. 'Tom tried to rub me out and I tried to rub him out – it was so funny.'

'Show me how funny it was,' said Mother, and she called Tom. Then the two boys showed her, giggling as they rubbed their cloths to and fro across the window, grinning at one another.

Mother laughed and laughed. 'Yes, it's very funny,' she said. 'Now would you both like to run down to the shop and buy yourselves an ice cream each for doing my window so nicely?'

Now you can't go on quarrelling with somebody you've giggled with. Every time Tom looked at Willie he laughed, and Willie kept giggling too.

'Yes, we'll go together,' said Tom. 'Come on, Willie.

Let's be friends again. I can't laugh with an enemy!'

'Nor can I!' said Willie. So they were friends again. Mother gave them a pound and they went off to buy their ice creams. On the way Willie was rather thoughtful.

'What's the matter?' asked Tom.

'I'm just thinking about Auntie,' said Willie. 'She's really very clever, Tom. She knew we would laugh over cleaning the same window – she knew we would try to rub each other out. It was her way of making us friends! Didn't I giggle too! I nearly choked with trying not to!'

Wasn't it a good idea that Tom's mother had? Now when the boys quarrel she looks at them and says, 'Do you remember how you cleaned that window together?' Then they giggle, of course, and everything is all right again!

The Old Bicycle

The Old Bicycle

PETER HAD a long way to go to school each morning. It took him half an hour to get there, so he had to start very early.

Some of the children went to school on bicycles, and Peter wished he could too. So when his birthday came near he asked his mother if she thought she could get him one.

'Mother, couldn't I possibly have one?' he begged. 'It would save me so much time. I get quite tired walking such a long way.'

'Peter, you can't ride a bicycle, so it's silly to ask for one,' said his mother.

This was quite true. Peter couldn't ride. He could ride Marjorie's tricycle, and he could easily pedal along in Jim's little motor car – but he couldn't ride a bicycle.

So he made up his mind to learn. On Saturday morning he went round to Jimmy's house and asked him if he could try to ride his bicycle.

'How do you ride it without falling off?' he asked.

'Well, if I were you, I'd try putting your right foot on the left pedal first, and use the bicycle like a scooter,' said Jimmy. 'Take hold of the handles – that's right – now put your foot on the left pedal – yes, like that. Now, off you go. Push yourself along with your left foot, and try to get your balance.'

So off went Peter round the garden, and he soon found that he could keep his balance very well like that. Then he put his right foot across to the right pedal, and the left foot on the left pedal and tried to see if he could balance like that too, with no foot on the ground at all. He couldn't at first and over he went. But he didn't hurt himself.

He tried again and again. He had to go home when dinnertime came. Jimmy said he could come in the afternoon and try again.

Well, it really wasn't very long before Peter had taught himself to ride on Jimmy's bike, and he was very pleased about it.

'Now Mother can't say I don't know how to ride!' he thought. So he spoke to her again.

'Mother, I can ride a bicycle now. I've learnt on Jimmy's. I can ride beautifully. So may I have a bicycle for my birthday, please?'

'Well, I'll talk to Daddy,' said Mother. 'But bicycles are very expensive things to buy, you know, Peter, and we haven't very much money.'

Mother spoke to Daddy that night, and the next day she told Peter what his father had said.

'Daddy says he can't possibly afford to buy you a bicycle,' she said. 'I'm sorry, Peter dear, because I know you'll be dreadfully disappointed after learning to ride – but it's no use expecting Daddy to buy you one, so don't hope for it.'

Peter *was* disappointed. He didn't say a word but he went up to his bedroom and screwed up his eyes to stop any tears from coming out. After all, he was soon going to be nine and he was far too big to cry about anything.

When his birthday came, his mother gave him a fine box of soldiers and his father gave him a book about aeroplanes. 'Sorry about the bicycle, old son,' said Daddy. 'I'd give it to you if I could, you know that. But I just can't afford it. I'm afraid you must go on walking to school.'

Now that very morning something happened to Peter. He was walking to school as usual when he saw a boy coming along on a bicycle. The bicycle was small and the boy was big. Just as the boy got near to Peter, a dog ran across the road in front of the bicycle.

The boy swerved, but the dog ran right into him. Over went the boy with a crash on to the ground, and the bicycle fell on top of him, its wheels spinning in the air! The dog gave a yelp and fled for its life.

Peter ran to help the boy up. But the boy could not stand.

'I've hurt my leg,' he said. 'I do hope it's not broken. Can you drag me to the side of the road?'

So Peter dragged him to the side and the boy took down his sock and looked at his poor leg. 'It hurts dreadfully,' he said. Peter knew that it must, because the big boy had tears in his eyes. No big boys ever cried unless they really couldn't help it.

'What shall I do?' said Peter. 'Where do you live?'

'Well, my father is Dr Johns,' said the boy. 'I'm Adam Johns. If you could possibly go to my home and catch my father before he starts out on his rounds, he could come along here at once in the car. But you'll have to be quick, because he is starting out early this morning.'

'But your house is ever so far!' said Peter. 'It will take me ages to get there, even if I run.'

'Can you ride a bike?' asked Adam. 'If you can, see if mine is all right. It doesn't look as if I smashed anything when I fell over.'

'Yes, I can ride,' said Peter. 'I've never ridden in the road before, but I can be careful. I'll go right away now and see if I can catch your father. Goodbye!'

Peter jumped on to Adam's bicycle. 'Just be careful now!' shouted Adam. 'I don't want *you* to have an accident too!'

Peter was careful. He rode well to the left of the road, and didn't take any risks at all. The bicycle was just the right size for him. It seemed rather an old one, for the paint was worn off, and the bright parts were rusty. Part of the rubber of the left pedal was missing, and the right brake wouldn't work. But it was lovely to ride a bicycle, even though it was an old one. Peter rang his bell at the corners, and at last came to Dr Johns' house. The doctor was just stepping into his car to go to see a patient.

Peter rode up, ringing his bell as loudly as possible.

The doctor turned round.

'Wait a minute, wait a minute!' shouted Peter. 'I've a message for you.'

Then he jumped off the bicycle and told the doctor what had happened to Adam. The doctor listened with a grave face. 'What a good thing you were able to ride a bicycle!' he said. 'You'd better ride to school on it this morning or you will be late. Thank you for your help. I'll go straight to Adam now.'

He set off in his car. Peter rode to school, being very careful indeed not to go too fast because of the broken brake.

He rode home on the bicycle too, and Mother was most astonished to see him arriving at the gate on a bicycle.

'Where did you get that from?' she asked. Peter told her.

'Mother, could I have my dinner quickly so that I can ride the bike back to Dr Johns and ask how Adam is?' he said. 'Then I can leave the bicycle there and walk to school in good time.'

'Very well,' said his mother. 'But don't gobble or you'll be ill!'

Peter soon finished his dinner. Then he went to his bookshelf and looked along his books. He thought perhaps Adam might like a book to read if he had to rest his leg – and perhaps he would like a jigsaw puzzle to do, too.

He put a book in the bicycle basket and a jigsaw puzzle. Then off he went, ringing the bell merrily at the corners. He soon came to Adam's house. He put the bicycle in the front garden and rang the doorbell.

The daily help showed him into the drawing room, and in a moment Adam's mother came into the room.

'You must be the boy who so kindly helped Adam this morning!' she said. 'Thank you very much indeed.'

'How is Adam's leg?' asked Peter.

'I'm afraid it is broken,' said Mrs Johns. 'But not very badly. And as you fetched help so quickly, it was set almost at once and will soon be mended.'

'I've brought Adam a book to read, and a puzzle,' said Peter. 'I'm really awfully sorry his leg is broken.'

'Oh, how kind you are!' said Mrs Johns. 'Come and see Adam. He is in his playroom.'

Peter was taken to see Adam. The big boy had a fine playroom with an electric railway running all round it.

It looked most exciting. Peter had a clockwork railway, but the electric one looked wonderful.

'Hallo!' said Adam. 'Did you hear my leg was broken? No wonder it hurt me!'

Peter gave Adam what he had brought. The two boys talked hard. 'You must come after tea and set my electric train going,' said Adam.

'Well, I would,' said Peter, 'but I'd have to walk, you see, and I'd never have time to get here and back and do my homework too. I haven't got a bike like you.'

'Haven't you?' said Mrs Johns. 'Well – Adam is having a new, much bigger bicycle for his birthday next week, and we were wondering what to do with his old one. Perhaps you would like to have it?'

'Good idea!' said Adam. 'Then you can come and see me every day! Yes – you have it, Peter. I can't ride for some weeks, and by that time my new bike will have arrived. So I can give you my old one with pleasure. You were jolly kind to me and you deserve it!'

Peter was red with delight. 'I shall have to ask my mother first,' he said. 'But I'm sure she'll say yes. Oh, I say – I have so badly wanted a bike, and now I've got one! I'll ride home on it and see what Mother says!'

Mother said yes, of course! 'You've been a good boy and not grumbled because we couldn't give you a bicycle for your birthday,' she said, 'and now that your own kindness has brought you one, I am certainly not going to say no. You may have it, and Daddy and I will get the brake mended for you, and a new rubber for the pedal, and have it all repainted. Then it will be as good as new!'

Well, you should see that old bicycle now! It looks

just like a new one, and Peter keeps it so bright and shining. He is very proud of it and rides on it to school every day.

'Your accident brought me two things!' he said to Adam. 'It brought me a bicycle – and a friend. Shan't we have fun together when your leg is better, Adam!'

Acknowledgements

All efforts have been made to seek necessary permissions.

The stories in this publication first appeared in the following publications:

'The Goblin Aeroplane' first appeared in *Sunny Stories for Little Folks*, No. 129, 1931.

'Billy-Bob has a Surprise' first appeared in *Billy-Bob Tales*, 1938.

'First Walk in July – St Swithin's Day' first appeared in *Enid Blyton's Nature Lover's Book*, 1944.

'The Enchanted Sea' first appeared in *Sunny Stories for Little Folks*, No. 126, 1931.

'A Knot in Twiddle's Hanky' first appeared in *Sunny Stories*, No. 414, 1947.

'The Fox and the Six Cats' first appeared in *Sunny Stories for Little Folks*, No. 119, 1931.

'Mister Meddle and the Bull' first appeared in *Enid Blyton's Sunny Stories*, No. 266, 1942.

'Mr Pink-Whistle's Party' first appeared in *Sunny Stories*, No. 478, 1950.

'Second Walk in July – Summer Holidays' first appeared in *Enid Blyton's Nature Lover's Book*, 1944.

'The Great Big Fish' first appeared in *Enid Blyton's Sunny Stories*, No. 25, 1937.

'Flip's Sunstroke' first appeared in *The Enid Blyton Book of Bunnies*, 1925.

'Nicky's Motor Car' first appeared as 'Derek's Motor-car' in *Enid Blyton's Sunny Stories*, No. 276, 1942.

'The Very Forgetful Gnome' first appeared in *Sunny Stories for Little Folks*, No. 236, 1936.

'Somebody Saw!' first appeared in *Safety Fun*, No. 5, 1951.

'The Little Paper-Folk' first appeared in *Sunny Stories for Little Folks*, No. 174, 1933.

'The Little Prickly Family' first appeared in *Sunny Stories for Little Folks*, No. 117, 1931.

ACKNOWLEDGEMENTS

'They Said He Was Too Small' first appeared in *Sunny Stories*, No. 520, 1951.

'When the Moon Was Blue' first appeared in *Sunny Stories for Little Folks*, No. 243, 1936.

'The Bumblebee Hums' first appeared in *Teacher's World*, No. 1,670, 1935.

'Andrew's Robin' first appeared in *Enid Blyton's Sunny Stories*, No. 90, 1938.

'The Two Cross Boys' first appeared in *Enid Blyton's Sunny Stories*, No. 193, 1940.

'The Old Bicycle' first appeared in *Enid Blyton's Sunny Stories*, No. 259, 1941.

327

Enid Blyton

is one of the most popular children's authors of all time. Her books have sold over 500 million copies and have been translated into other languages more often than any other children's author.

Enid Blyton adored writing for children. She wrote over 600 books and hundreds of short stories. *The Famous Five* books, now 75 years old, are her most popular. She is also the author of other favourites including *The Secret Seven*, *The Magic Faraway Tree*, *Malory Towers* and *Noddy*.

Born in London in 1897, Enid lived much of her life in Buckinghamshire and adored dogs, gardening and the countryside. She was very knowledgeable about trees, flowers, birds and animals. Dorset — where some of the Famous Five's adventures are set — was a favourite place of hers too.

Enid Blyton's stories are read and loved by millions of children (and grown-ups) all over the world. Visit enidblyton.com to discover more.